Match Mine

Mathematics

Concept and Development
Miguel Kagan

Illustrations
Erin Kant
Jeremie Rujanawech

Publisher
Kagan Publishing

Kagan

Kagan Publishing
981 Calle Amanecer
San Clemente, CA 92673
1 (800) 933-2667
www.KaganOnline.com

ISBN: 978-1-879097-22-3

Table of Contents

30 Match Mine Games!

Games Categorized by Mathematics Standards

 Numbers and Operations

 **Alegebra**

 **Geometry**

The standards presented here and throughout this book are adapted from the National Council of Teachers of Mathematics.

Match Mine: Mathematics
Kagan Publishing • 1 (800) 933-2667 • www.KaganOnline.com

Measurement

Data Analysis and Probability

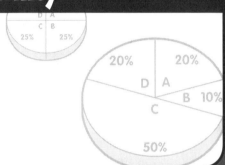

Problem Solving

Communication

All Match Mine games develop mathematical thinking and communication.
Instructional programs from prekindergarten through grade 12 should enable all students to:
- organize and consolidate their mathematical thinking through communication.
- communicate their mathematical thinking coherently and clearly to peers, teachers, and others.
- analyze and evaluate the mathematical thinking and strategies of others.
- use the language of mathematics to express mathematical ideas precisely.

How to Play
Match Mine

Partners, on opposite sides of a barrier, must communicate with precision so the Receiver can match the Sender's arrangement of game pieces on a game board.

Sender

Receiver

Students pair up. Partners sit on opposite sides of a barrier so they can't see each other's game board. They each have an identical game board and identical game pieces. One student is the "Sender" and the other is the "Receiver." To start, the Sender first lays out all of his/her game pieces on the game board in any arrangement without talking to the Receiver. The Sender cannot move the game pieces once they are all set in place. The object of the game is for the Sender and Receiver to communicate clearly so the Receiver can perfectly match the Sender's arrangement. To make a match, the Sender describes his/her arrangement by explaining the location of each game piece. The Receiver listens carefully and follows the Sender's directions. On the following pages, you will find detailed instructions, and game variations.

Match Mine: Mathematics
Kagan Publishing • 1 (800) 933-2667 • www.KaganOnline.com

Getting Ready

Partners—one the Sender, the other the Receiver—sit on opposite sides of a barrier with identical game boards and game pieces.

1. Sender Creates Arrangement

The Sender arranges his/her game pieces on his/her game board while the Receiver waits quietly. For the Money game (game 19 on page 87), the Sender places his/her coins in the piggy banks.

2. Sender Directs Receiver

The Sender gives the Receiver directions to match the Sender's arrangement of game pieces on the game board. Instructions may sound like: "Eighty-one cents is in the top middle piggy bank. Below eighty-one cents on the left is the piggy bank with thirty-eight cents…"

3. Partners Check

When finished, partners carefully set their game boards side by side to check for accuracy. "OK, it sounds like we have a match, let's check."

4. Praise and Plan

The Receiver praises the Sender for his/her instructions and they develop improvement strategies. "Great job describing your money layout. Next time, let's call twenty-five cents a quarter."

5. Switch Roles

The Receiver now becomes the Sender and the Sender becomes the Receiver. The pair plays again.

Match Mine

Introduction

Why Play Match Mine?

The games in this book are specifically designed to build mathematical knowledge, skills, and vocabulary. They are ideal for developing mathematical thinking and communication skills in a fun, game-like format. In addition, Match Mine yields many important learning benefits for students:

- Develops mathematical vocabulary
- Improves verbal communication
- Enhances ability to give directions
- Promotes active listening
- Nurtures cooperative skills
- Promotes role-taking ability
- Develops visual analysis
- Increases spatial vocabulary (right, left, top, etc.)

Ways to Play

• Whole Class Activity

The whole class can play Match Mine at the same time. Each pair receives a Match Mine game set.

• Learning Center

Match Mine can be done at a center. At a center, you may have two of the same games set up to accommodate four students. At another center, there may be different games.

• Sponge Activity

Match Mine is a great activity students can play when they've finished their work.

What's in this Book?

Intro Page ••••••••••

For each of the 30 games in this book, you will find an introduction page that shows the game board and game pieces, and lists related vocabulary. The vocabulary is either vocabulary the game develops or related vocabulary you may teach students before they play, so they practice using the mathematical vocabulary as they play. The Challenger is included to differentiate instruction, and make the game more challenging for older and/ or more skilled students.

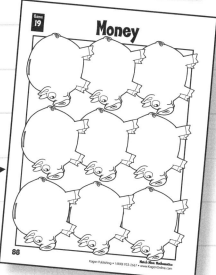

Game Board ••••••••••

Each of the 30 games has a unique game board. The game board is a reproducible page. Make one copy of the game board for each student playing (2 game boards per pair).

Game Pieces ••••••••••

There is an identical set of game pieces for Partner A and Partner B. If they fit, the game pieces for both partners are on the same page. Otherwise, the game pieces are on two pages, one set per page. Make a copy of the game pieces so each student receives an identical set. Students cut out each game piece.

Playing Tips

Sponge Activity

Pairs will finish at different rates. When they're done, let them play a different Match Mine game or play the same game using a variation described on the following pages.

Creating a Barrier

A barrier is set up between each pair. The preferred barrier is a file folder barrier. To make a file folder barrier, you will need two file folders and a paper clip. Place the file folders back to back, and paper clip the top of the file folders together as illustrated. Next, open the file folders and spread out the bases so the barrier is self-standing. Instead of a paper clip, you can use staples or tape to keep the file folders together, but the paper clip doubles for a storage closure as described on page 14.

Color Cardstock Paper

Copy the game board and game pieces on different colored paper. Cardstock is preferable if available because it makes the game more durable for re-use. Having a different colored game board and game pieces makes the game pieces easier to see.

Laminate Games

For extra durability, laminate the game board and game pieces. Laminate the game pieces before they are cut out.

Model it

To introduce Match Mine to the class, model it using either an overhead projector or role play it.

Overhead Method: Provide each student with a game board and game pieces. Copy the game board onto a sheet of transparency film and copy the game pieces onto another sheet (preferably colored film).

With the projector turned off, first arrange your game pieces on your game board and then give directions to the class. Each student builds his/her own game board. When it is time to check

Alternative Barriers

Any barrier will work as long as students can hear each other, but can't see each other's game board or game pieces. Alternate barrier options include the following:
• Large book
• Binder
• Students sit back to back

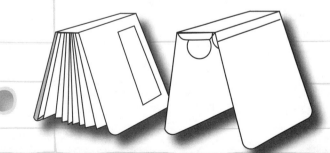

how well the students have matched your arrangement, turn on the overhead projector.

Role-Play Method: You role play with another student. The student is the Sender and you are the Receiver. Play dumb, purposefully misinterpreting vague directions. An example: If the student says, "Place the circle on top of the square," you place the circle directly over the square, covering it up! The student meant above the square. If there is any ambiguity in the student's instructions, intentionally "go wrong" to demonstrate the importance of precise directions.

Playing to Learn
Students can come up with strategies to successfully make a match without developing their math and vocabulary skills. For example, they may say, "I organized the pieces from biggest to smallest." Although this is quite clever, the real intent of the game is to use the target vocabulary. Tell students that the true goal is to build math skills and vocabulary, so they should try to be as descriptive and accurate as possible.

Do the Walkabout
As students play in pairs, walk around and eavesdrop on them. This is a great time to make corrections. If you notice similar problems, stop the class and make an adjustment.

Checking for Accuracy
When students think they made a match, they check for accuracy. The best way to check is for the Receiver to carefully move his/her game board side by side with the Sender's game board. Then, they check each game piece and pat each other on the back or do some celebration for each correct piece. If they are not side by side and do not check each piece, they may think they have made a match when in actuality they haven't.

Processing Errors
If students find a error, they discuss why they made an error. Was the wrong vocabulary used? Was a direction not followed or interpreted correctly? Students find where they made a mistake and discuss how they can communicate more clearly next time.

Match Mine

Variations

not allowed to peek at the answers on the back. Students use the written description to try to make a match. When they think they have it correct, they flip over the instructions and compare their arrangement with the answer.

Single Sender

Match Mine can be played as a whole class with a single Sender. The Sender can be the teacher or one student. The rest of the class are the Receivers. The Sender (at the overhead) builds an arrangement, and describes it to the whole class. The Receivers follow the Sender's instructions. Because the whole-class format cuts down on active participation, it is suggested only for younger students or for initial demonstrations.

Pass-A-Note

Students write directions, passing notes back and forth, communicating only in writing.

Arrange-What-I-Write

Every student gets an extra game board, so they each have two game boards and one set of game pieces. They each arrange their game pieces on one game board. On the second game board, they make a note of the location of each game piece. Then, they each describe their arrangement as fully as possible in writing on the back of the game board (no drawing allowed). Students then switch instructions. Tell them they are

Teams of Four

Match Mine may also be played in teams. Each team is provided two sets of game pieces, two game boards, and one barrier. Pairs are seated on each side of the barrier with their game board and game pieces. One pair is designated as Senders, the other as Receivers. For equal participation, the two Senders alternate giving instructions. Receivers discuss placing the game pieces and alternate placing them.

Silent Partner

To add a degree of difficulty, introduce a fun variation called "Silent Partner." In this variation, only the Sender is allowed to speak. The Receiver cannot ask for clarification during the game. This requires precise instructions and active listening.

Taking Turns

Instead of the Sender building a design and the Receiver matching the design, partners take turns placing each piece. They alternate roles of Sender and Receiver after placing each game piece.

Yes or No

Yes or No borrows from the game 20 Questions. The Sender builds an arrangement. When done, the Receiver tries to match the layout. As in the game 20 Questions, the Reciever may only ask the Sender "Yes" or "No" questions.

Is the sphere above the cube?

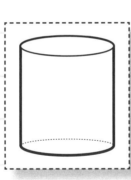

Is the cylinder next to the octahedron?

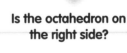

Is the octahedron on the right side?

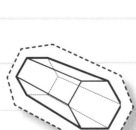

Is the hexagonal prism in the center?

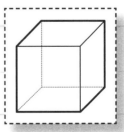

Is the cube on the left side of the torus?

Storage Tips

We recommend using file folders as barriers because they fold flat, ideal for storage. When students are done playing, have them place their game pieces in separate envelopes or resealable sandwich bags. Then, they fold the barriers closed with the game boards and game pieces bags inside and use the paper clip to hold it all together. Store the class set together. If you store your Match Mine games this way, it makes it quick and easy to pass out the games and set them up again for the next use.

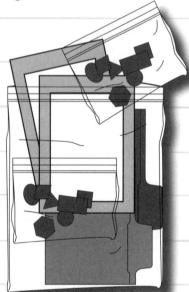

Put Away Each Game Separately
- Place game pieces in 2 separate resealable, plastic sandwich bags or envelopes
- Fold game boards into file folders
- Paper clip the set together
- Insert the entire set into a large resealable, plastic bag or catalog envelope

Match Mine

Store Games Together
Keep all the same games together and label the class set so they are ready for next time!

Angle Degrees

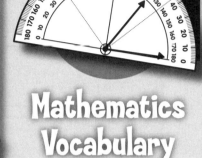

Partner A places angle pieces on the protractor game board. Partner B cooperates with Partner A to make a match.

Game Board

Game Pieces

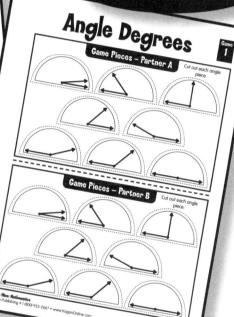

Mathematics Vocabulary

- Acute angle
- Angle
- Arms of the angle
- Base line
- Degrees
- Inner scale
- Intersect
- Lines
- Obtuse angle
- Outer scale
- Protractor
- Right angle
- Straight angle
- Vertex

Challenger

The Sender must state if each angle is acute, obtuse, right, or straight as its location is described to the Receiver. For example, "The 90° right angle is in the top left protractor."

Measurement Standard

Apply appropriate techniques, tools, and formulas to determine measurements.

Students should...

- select and apply appropriate standard units and tools to measure length, area, volume, weight, time, temperature, and the size of angles.
- select and use benchmarks to estimate measurements.

Angle Degrees

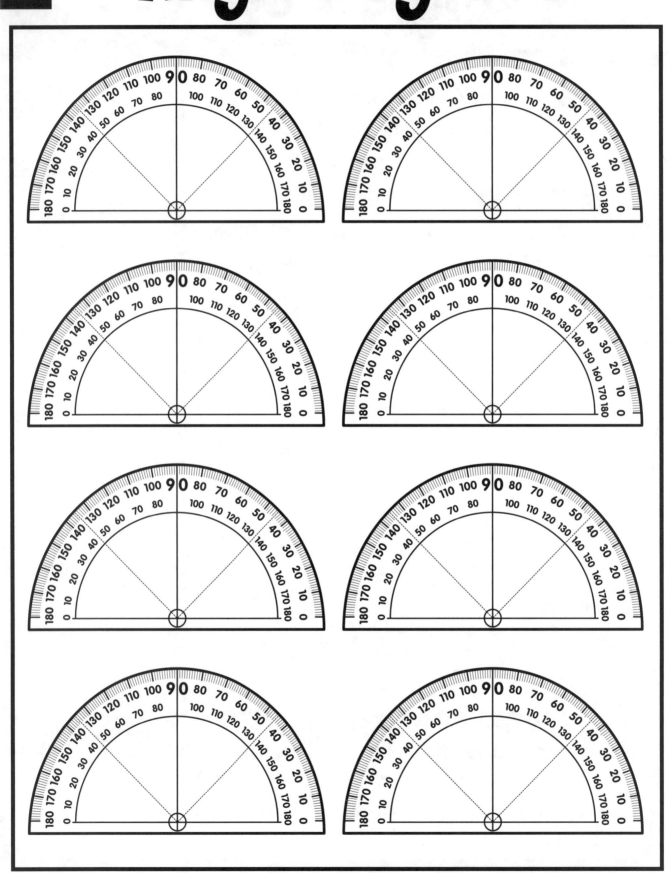

Angle Degrees

Game Pieces – Partner A

Cut out each angle piece.

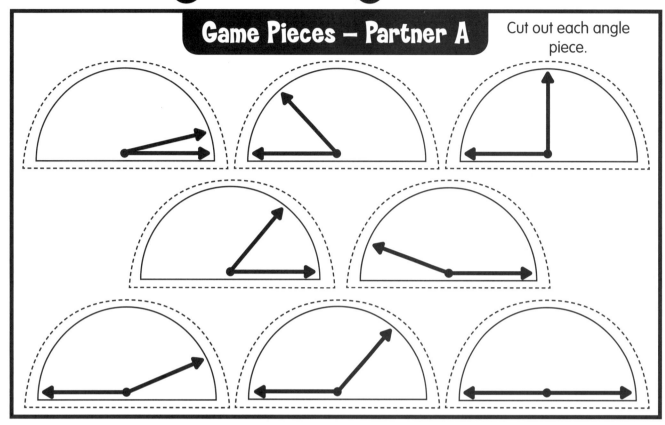

Game Pieces – Partner B

Cut out each angle piece.

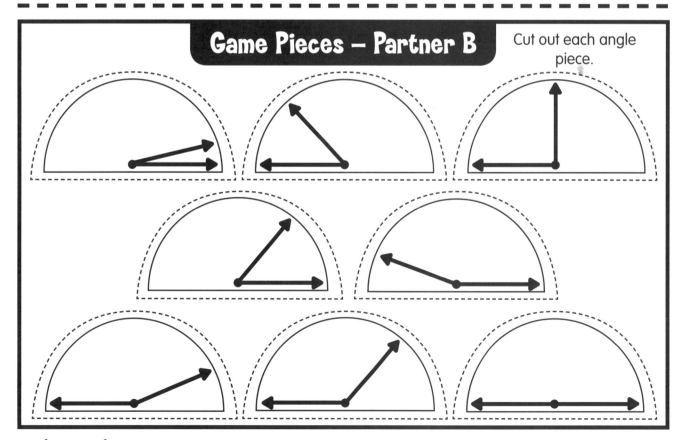

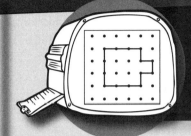

Partner A places area pieces on the measuring tape game board. Partner B cooperates with Partner A to make a match.

Game Board

Game Pieces

Mathematics Vocabulary

- Across
- Area
- Dots
- Down
- Grid
- Line
- Shape
- Square
- Units

Challenger

The Sender must determine and state the area (in square units) of each piece as its location is described to the Receiver. For example, "The piece that is 10 square units, and is shaped like a square plus one more square unit, is in the bottom right measuring tape."

Measurement Standard

- Understand measurable attributes of objects and the units, systems, and processes of measurement.
- Apply appropriate techniques, tools, and formulas to determine measurements.

Students should...

- understand such attributes as length, area, weight, volume, and size of angle and select the appropriate type of unit for measuring each attribute.
- explore what happens to measurements of a two-dimensional shape, such as its perimeter and area, when the shape is changed in some way.
- select and apply appropriate standard units and tools to measure length, area, volume, weight, time, temperature, and the size of angles.

Area

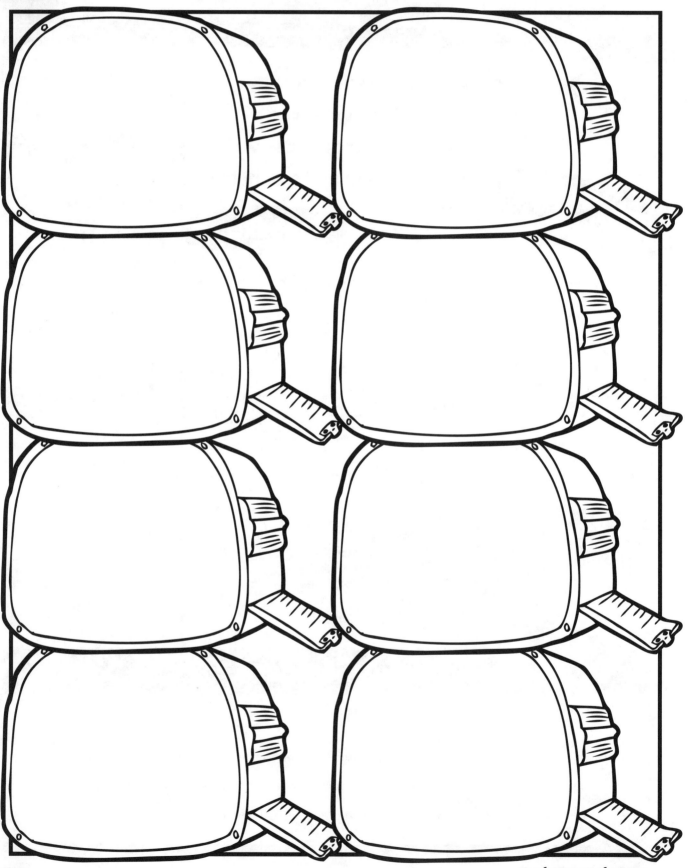

Match Mine: Mathematics
Kagan Publishing • 1 (800) 933-2667 • www.KaganOnline.com

Area

Game Pieces – Partner A

Cut out each area piece.

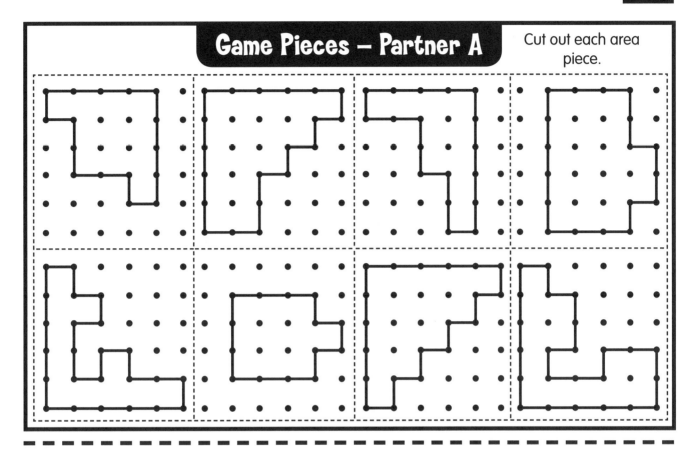

Game Pieces – Partner B

Cut out each area piece.

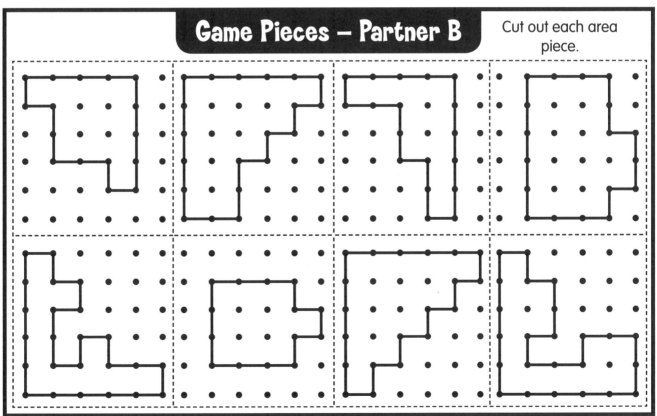

Arrays

Partner A places array pieces on the bubble game board. Partner B cooperates with Partner A to make a match.

Game Board

Game Pieces

Mathematics Vocabulary

- By
- Column
- Commutative
- Multiply
- Product
- Row
- Times

Challenger

The Sender must state the multiplication problem each array represents as its location is described to the Receiver. For example, "The array that represents 3 x 4 = 12 is in the bottom center bubble."

➕ Numbers and Operations Standard

Understand meanings of operations and how they relate to one another.
Students should...
- understand various meanings of multiplication and division.
- understand the effects of multiplying and dividing whole numbers.

Arrays

Match Mine: Mathematics

Kagan Publishing • 1 (800) 933-2667 • www.KaganOnline.com

Arrays

Game Pieces – Partner A

Cut out each array.

Game Pieces – Partner B

Cut out each array.

> Partner A places base 10 pieces on the popcorn game board. Partner B cooperates with Partner A to make a match.

Game Board

Base 10

POPCORN

28

Game Pieces

Base 10

Game Pieces – Partner A — Cut out each base 10 piece.

29

Mathematics Vocabulary

- Flats
- Hundred
- One
- Rods
- Ten
- Units

 **Challenger**

The Sender must state the number the Base 10 pieces represent as its location is described to the Receiver. For example, "The piece that represents 221 is in the middle center popcorn."

✚ Numbers and Operations Standard

Understand numbers, ways of representing numbers, relationships among numbers, and number systems. **Students should...**

- understand the place-value structure of the base-ten number system and be able to represent and compare whole numbers and decimals.

Base 10

Base 10

Game Pieces – Partner A

Cut out each base 10 piece.

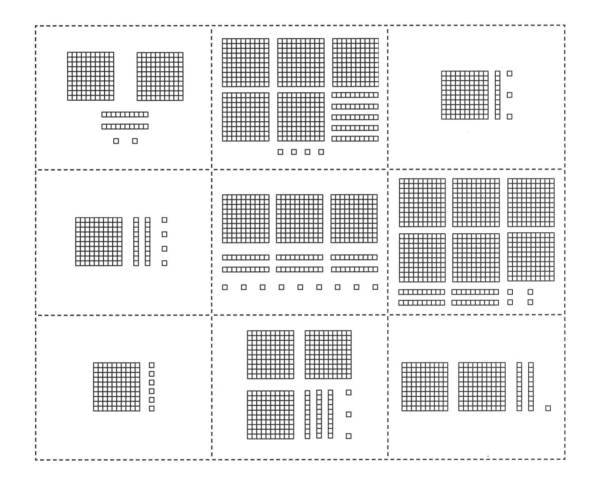

Base 10

Game Pieces – Partner B
Cut out each base 10 piece.

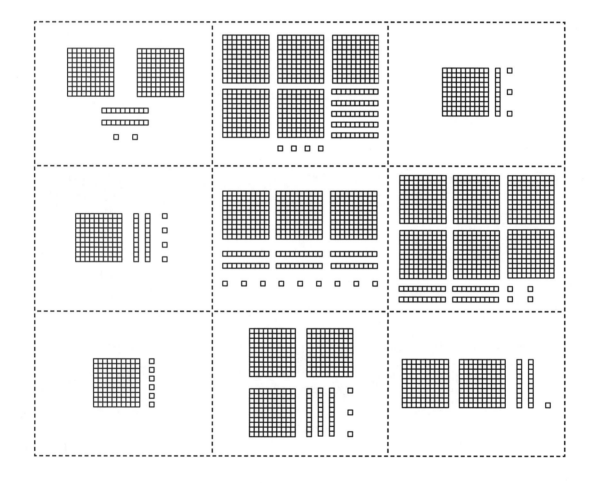

Match Mine: Mathematics
Kagan Publishing • 1 (800) 933-2667 • www.KaganOnline.com

Calendar

Partner A places calendar pieces on the calendar game board. Partner B cooperates with Partner A to make a match.

Game Board

Game Pieces

Mathematics Vocabulary

- First–Thirtieth
- Friday
- Last
- Monday
- Saturday
- Sunday
- Thursday
- Tuesday
- Wednesday

Challenger

The Sender may not state a date when describing the location of a calendar icon to the Receiver. For example, "The baseball game is on the last Saturday of the month."

Problem Solving Standard

Instructional programs from prekindergarten through grade 12:
Students should...
- solve problems that arise in mathematics and in other contexts.

Match Mine: Mathematics
Kagan Publishing • 1 (800) 933-2667 • www.KaganOnline.com

Calendar

APRIL

Sunday	Monday	Tuesday	Wednesday	Thursday	Friday	Saturday
1	2	3	4	5	6	7
8	9	10	11	12	13	14
15	16	17	18	19	20	21
22	23	24	25	26	27	28
29	30					

Match Mine: Mathematics
Kagan Publishing • 1 (800) 933-2667 • www.KaganOnline.com

Calendar

Game Pieces – Partner A

Cut out each calendar icon.

Game Pieces – Partner B

Cut out each calendar icon.

Capacity

Partner A places capacity pieces on the gallon game board. Partner B cooperates with Partner A to make a match.

Mathematics Vocabulary

- Cup
- Customary System
- Fluid ounces
- Gallon
- Pint
- Quart

Game Board

Game Pieces

Challenger

The Sender must state the total fluid ounces illustrated on each piece broken down by each cup, pint, and quart as its location is described to the Receiver. For example, "The piece with 96 ounces in quarts and 32 ounces in pints is in the middle row on the right side."

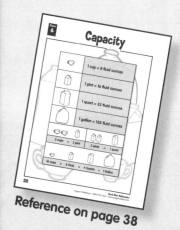

Reference on page 38

Measurement Standard

Understand measurable attributes of objects and the units, systems, and processes of measurement.
Students should...
- understand the need for measuring with standard units and become familiar with standard units in the customary and metric systems.

Capacity

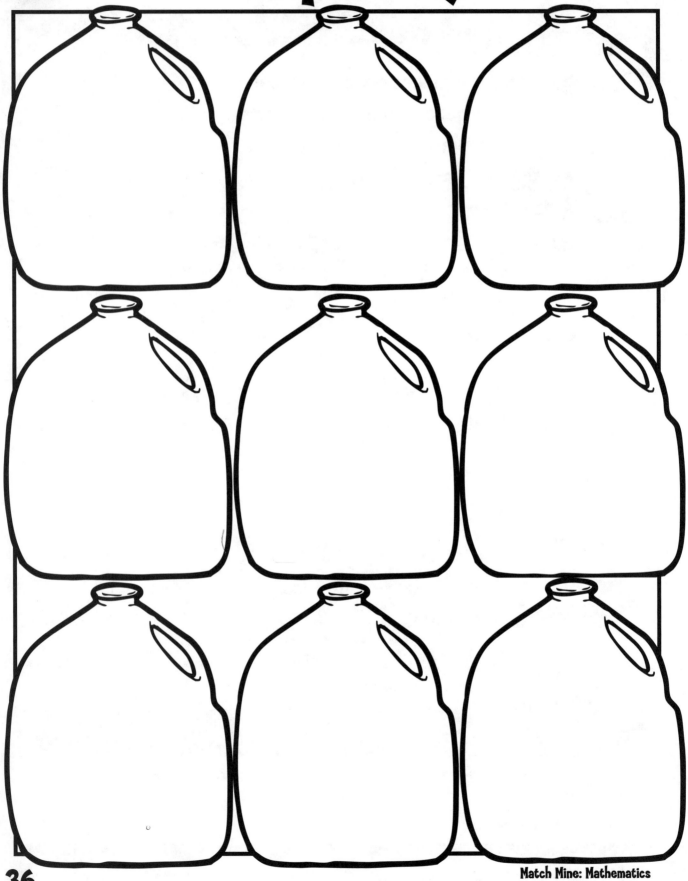

Match Mine: Mathematics
Kagan Publishing • 1 (800) 933-2667 • www.KaganOnline.com

Capacity

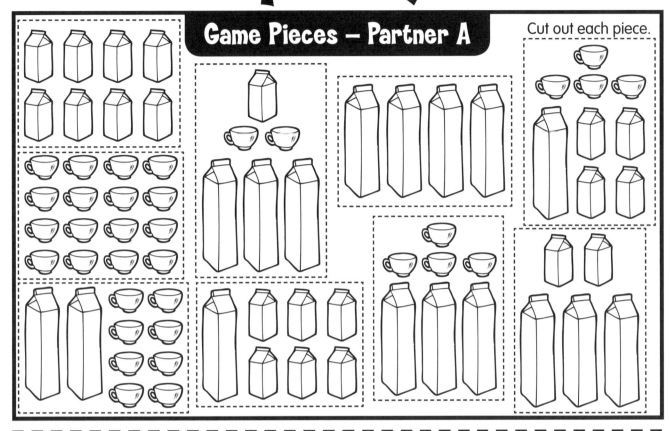

Game Pieces – Partner A

Cut out each piece.

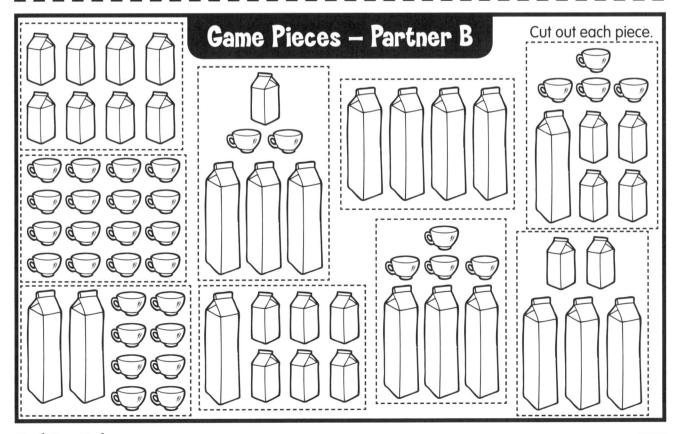

Game Pieces – Partner B

Cut out each piece.

Capacity

	1 cup = 8 fluid ounces
	1 pint = 16 fluid ounces
	1 quart = 32 fluid ounces
	1 gallon = 128 fluid ounces

2 cups = 1 pint	**2 pints = 1 quart**

16 cups   =   8 Pints   =   4 Quarts   =   1 Gallon

Match Mine: Mathematics
Kagan Publishing • 1 (800) 933-2667 • www.KaganOnline.com

Coordinate–Plane

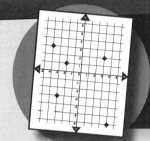

Partner A places letter and number pieces on the coordinate plane game board. Partner B cooperates with Partner A to make a match.

Game Board

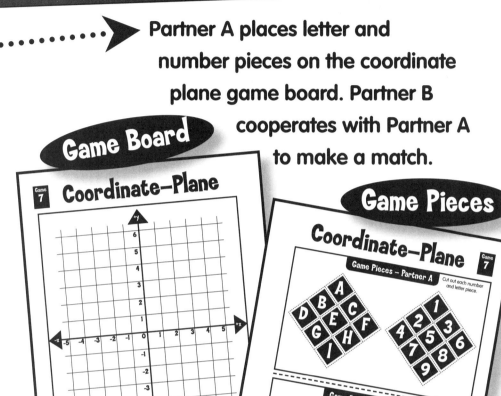

Game Pieces

Mathematics Vocabulary

- Cartesian plane
- Coordinate
- Coordinate plane
- Horizontal
- Negative
- Number line
- Ordered pair
- Origin
- Plot
- Positive
- Quadrant
- René Descartes
- *x*-axis
- *y*-axis

Challenger

The Sender must write the coordinate on a slip of paper and pass it to the Receiver without talking. For example, "A = (-2,3)."

Geometry Standard

Specify locations and describe spatial relationships using coordinate geometry and other representational systems.

Students should...
- describe location and movement using common language and geometric vocabulary.
- make and use coordinate systems to specify locations and to describe paths.

Coordinate–Plane

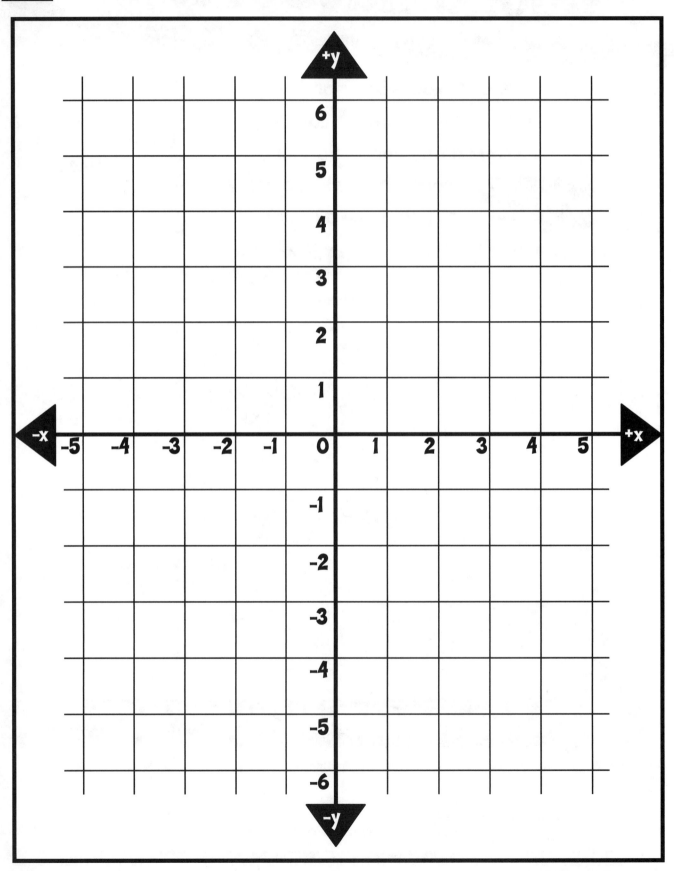

Match Mine: Mathematics
Kagan Publishing • 1 (800) 933-2667 • www.KaganOnline.com

Coordinate-Plane

Game Pieces – Partner A

Cut out each number and letter piece.

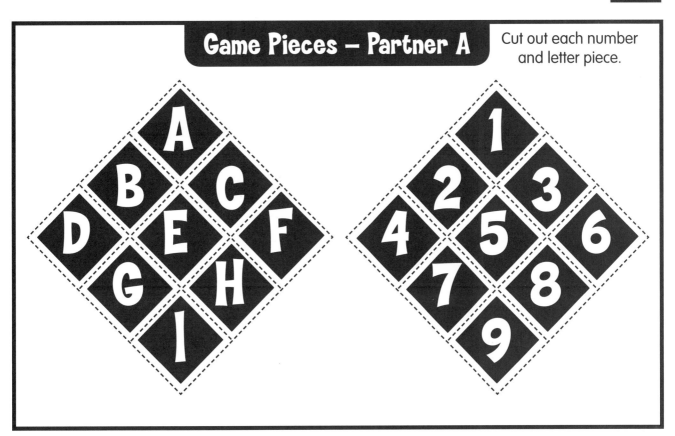

Game Pieces – Partner B

Cut out each number and letter piece.

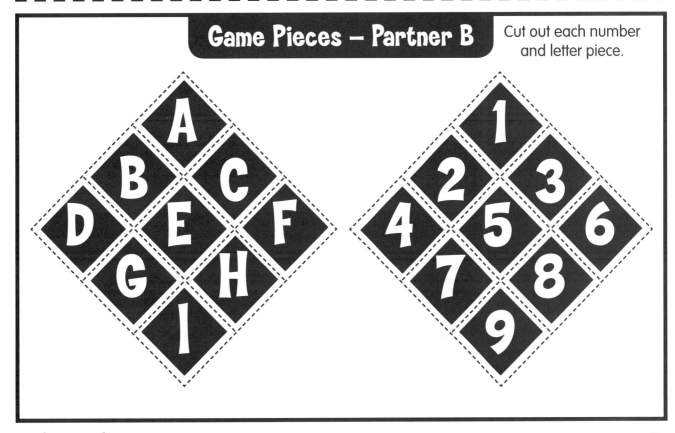

Coordinate-Points

Partner A places game coordinate point pieces on the graph game board. Partner B cooperates with Partner A to make a match.

Game Board

Coordinate-Points
Game 8

44

Kagan Publishing • 1(800) 933-2667 • www

Game Pieces

Coordinate-Points
Game 8

Game Pieces – Partner A
Cut out each coordinate points piece.

45

Mathematics Vocabulary

- Cartesian plane
- Coordinate
- Coordinate points
- Horizontal
- Negative
- Number line
- Ordered pair
- Origin
- Plot
- Positive
- Quadrant
- René Descartes
- *x*-axis
- *y*-axis

Challenger

The Sender must use *x*-axis and *y*-axis terminology to identify the point as its location is described to the Receiver. For example, "The piece that has a point at 5 on the *y*-axis and 5 on the *x*-axis is in the first box."

Geometry Standard

Specify locations and describe spatial relationships using coordinate geometry and other representational systems.
Students should...
- describe location and movement using common language and geometric vocabulary.
- make and use coordinate systems to specify locations and to describe paths.

Coordinate–Points

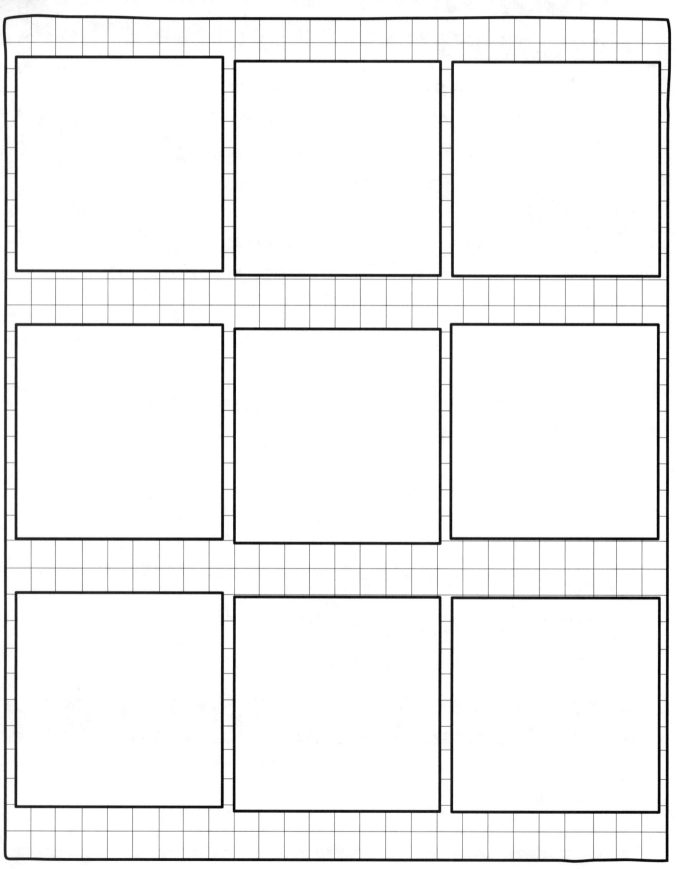

Match Mine: Mathematics
Kagan Publishing • 1 (800) 933-2667 • www.KaganOnline.com

Coordinate–Points

Game Pieces – Partner A

Cut out each coordinate point piece.

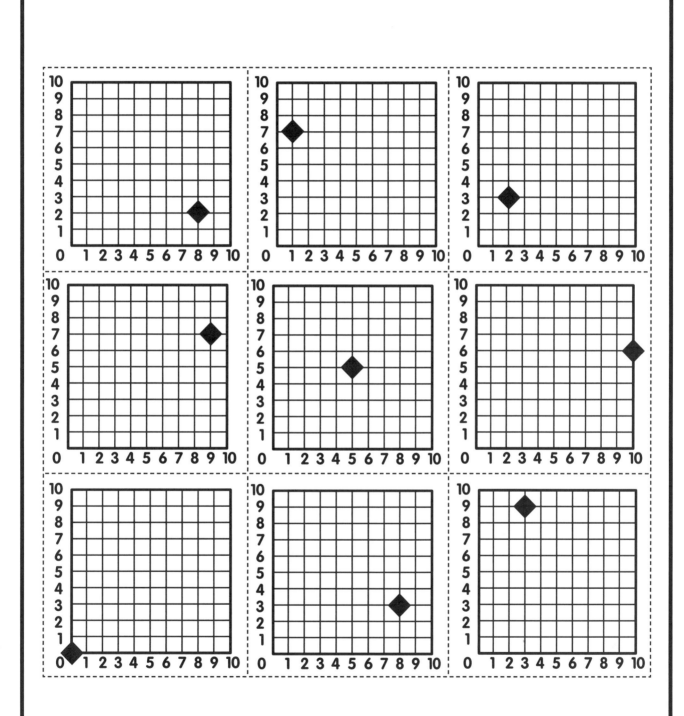

Coordinate—Points

Game Pieces – Partner B   Cut out each coordinate point piece.

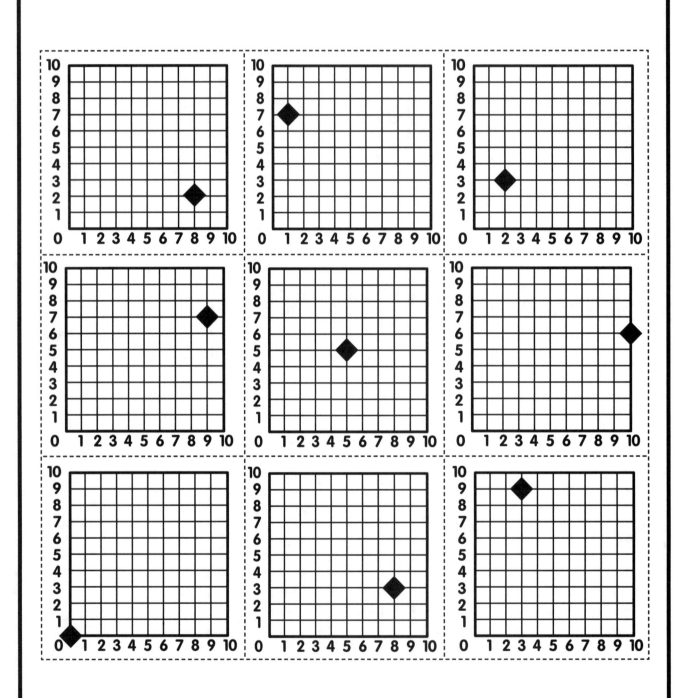

Match Mine: Mathematics
Kagan Publishing • 1 (800) 933-2667 • www.KaganOnline.com

Counting Cubes

Partner A places cube pieces on the ice cube game board. Partner B cooperates with Partner A to make a match.

Game Board

Game Pieces

Mathematics Vocabulary

- 3-D
- Back
- Block
- Bottom
- Cube
- Face
- First
- Front
- Left
- Middle
- Right
- Second
- Side
- Third
- Three-dimensional
- Top

Challenger

The Sender must state how many blocks are missing from a 27-block cube to describe the piece's location to the Receiver. For example, "The piece that has 8 blocks missing is in the first row, second column."

Geometry Standard

Analyze characteristics and properties of two- and three-dimensional geometric shapes and develop mathematical arguments about geometric relationships.
Students should...
- identify, compare, and analyze attributes of two-and three-dimensional shapes and develop vocabulary to describe the attributes.

Counting Cubes

Match Mine: Mathematics
Kagan Publishing • 1 (800) 933-2667 • www.KaganOnline.com

Counting Cubes

Game Pieces – Partner A

Cut out each cube piece.

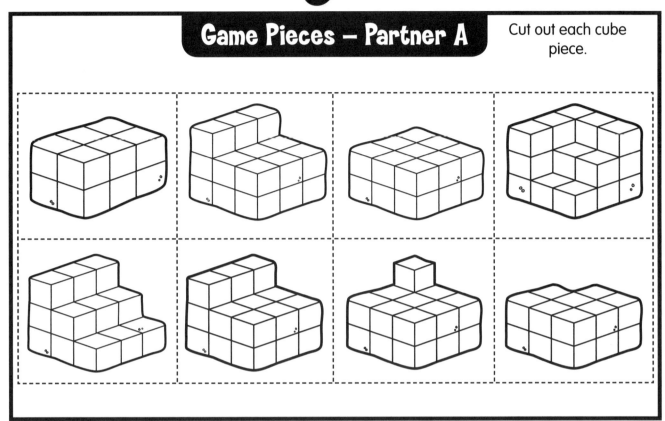

Game Pieces – Partner B

Cut out each cube piece.

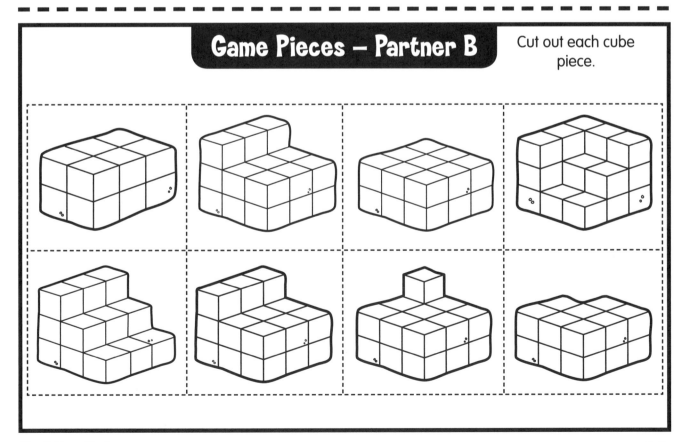

Partner A places jelly bean jar pieces on the jelly bean jar game board. Partner B cooperates with Partner A to make a match.

Game Board

Game Pieces

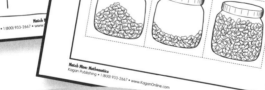

Mathematics Vocabulary

- Approximately
- Empty
- Estimate
- Full
- Half
- Percent estimate
- Quarter
- Roughly
- Rounding

Challenger

The Sender must use percent estimates to describe the piece's location to the Receiver. For example, "The jar that is approximately 50% full is in the second row, second column."

✚ Number and Operations Standard

Compute fluently and make reasonable estimates.
Students should...
- develop and use strategies to estimate the results of whole-number computations and to judge the reasonableness of such results.

Game
10

Estimating

Match Mine: Mathematics
Kagan Publishing • 1 (800) 933-2667 • www.KaganOnline.com

Estimating

Game Pieces – Partner A Cut out each jelly bean jar piece.

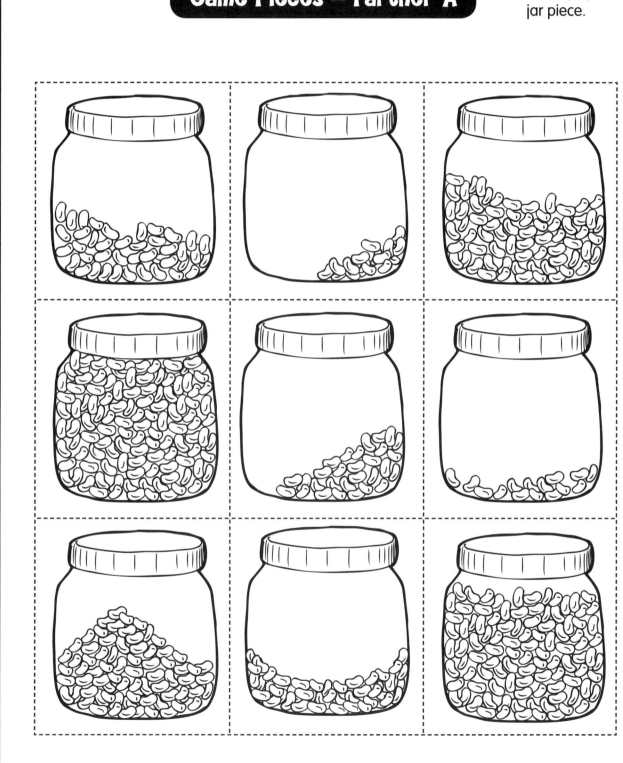

Estimating

Game Pieces – Partner B

Cut out each jelly bean jar piece.

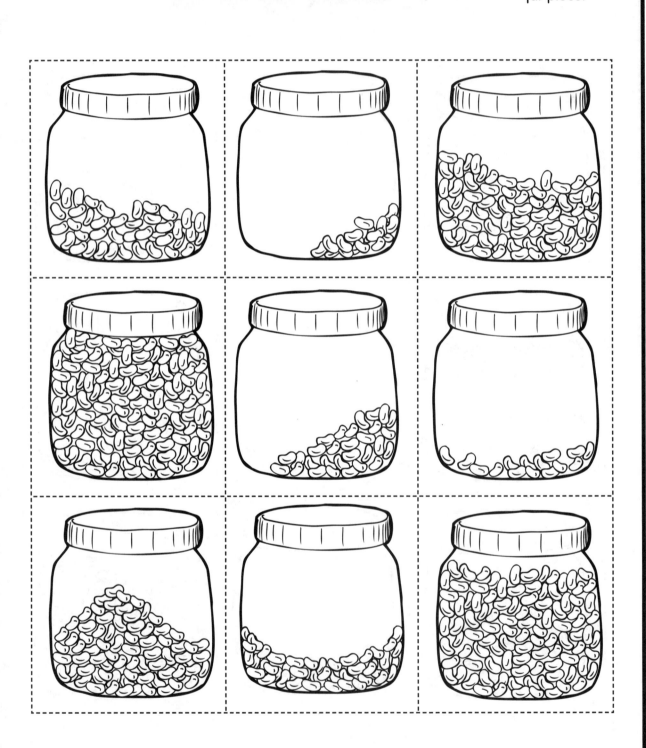

Fractions—Identifying

Partner A places pizza pieces on the pizza pan game board. Partner B cooperates with Partner A to make a match.

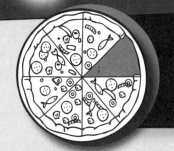

Game Board

Fractions—Identifying

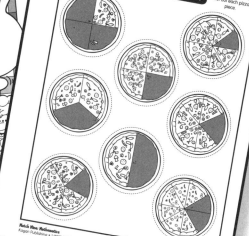

Game Pieces

Fractions—Identifying

Game Pieces – Partner A

Mathematics Vocabulary

- one-eighth (1/8)
- one-fifth (1/5)
- one-fourth (1/4)
- one-half (1/2)
- one-sixth (1/6)
- one-third (1/3)
- three-fourths (3/4)
- two-eighths (2/8)

Challenger

The Sender must convert the percent into a decimal as its location is described to the Receiver. For example, "The pizza that is 75% eaten is in the 8th pan."

✚ Number and Operations Standard

Understand numbers, ways of representing numbers, relationships among numbers, and number systems.

Students should...

- develop understanding of fractions as parts of unit wholes, as parts of a collection, as locations on number lines, and as divisions of whole numbers.
- use models, benchmarks, and equivalent forms to judge the size of fractions.

Fractions—Identifying

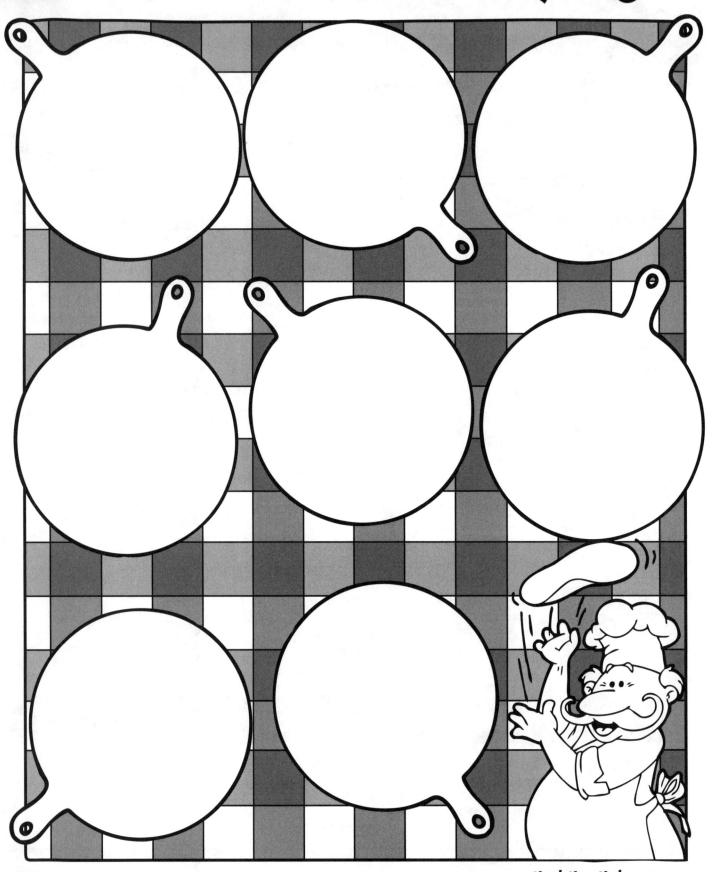

Match Mine: Mathematics
Kagan Publishing • 1 (800) 933-2667 • www.KaganOnline.com

Fractions–Identifying

Game Pieces – Partner A

Cut out each pizza piece.

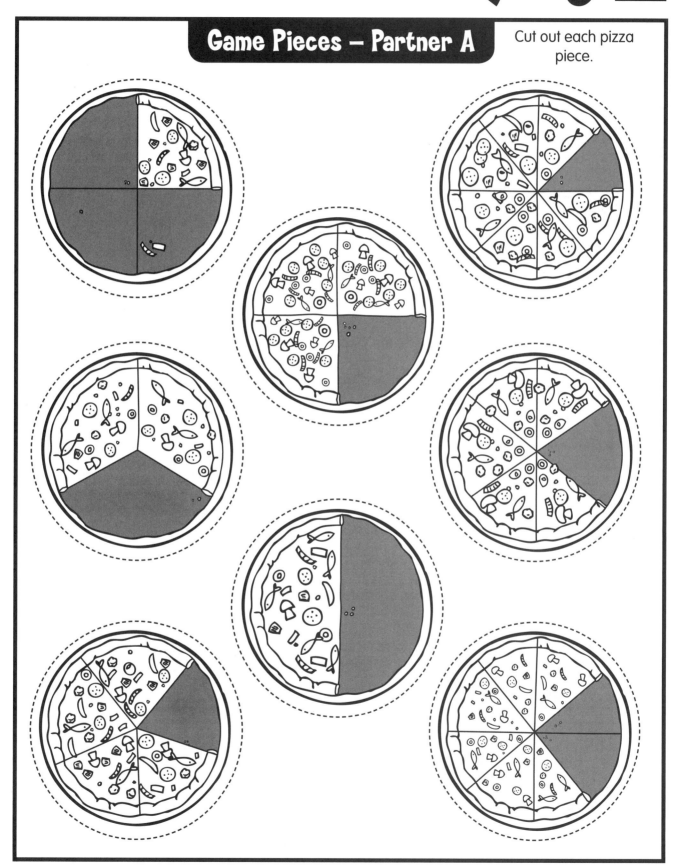

Fractions–Identifying

Game Pieces – Partner B

Cut out each pizza piece.

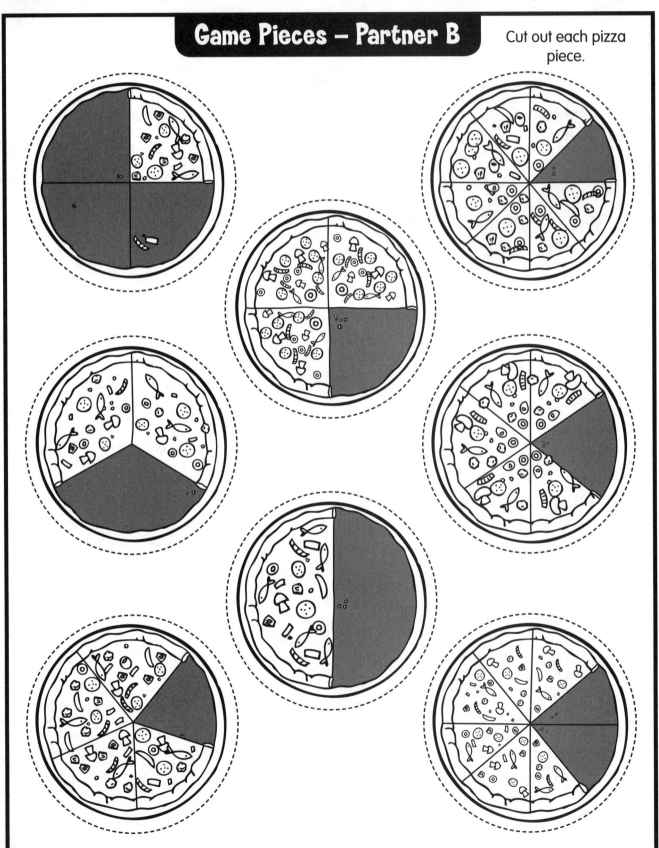

Match Mine: Mathematics
Kagan Publishing • 1 (800) 933-2667 • www.KaganOnline.com

Fractions–Naming

Partner A places gumballs on the gumball machine game board. Partner B cooperates with Partner A to make a match.

Game Board

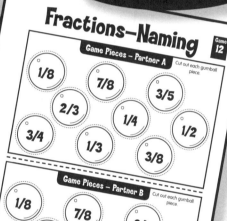

Game 12 Fractions–Naming

60

Game Pieces

Fractions–Naming **Game 12**

Game Pieces – Partner A Cut out each gumball piece.

1/8   7/8   3/5
2/3   1/4
3/4   1/2
1/3   3/8

Game Pieces – Partner B Cut out each gumball piece.

1/8   7/8   3/5
2/3   1/4
3/4   1/2
1/3   3/8

Match Mine: Mathematics
Kagan Publishing • 1 (800) 933-2667 • www.KaganOnline.com

61

Mathematics Vocabulary

- one-eighth (1/8)
- one-fourth (1/4)
- one-half (1/2)
- one-third (1/3)
- seven-eighths (7/8)
- three-eighths (3/8)
- three-fifths (3/5)
- three-fourths (3/4)
- two-thirds (2/3)

Challenger

The Sender must convert the percent into a decimal as its location is described to the Receiver. For example, "The gumball with the fraction that represents 50% is the highest gumball in the machine."

➕ Number and Operations Standard

Understand numbers, ways of representing numbers, relationships among numbers, and number systems.
Students should...
- recognize and generate equivalent forms of commonly used fractions, decimals, and percents.

Fractions—Naming

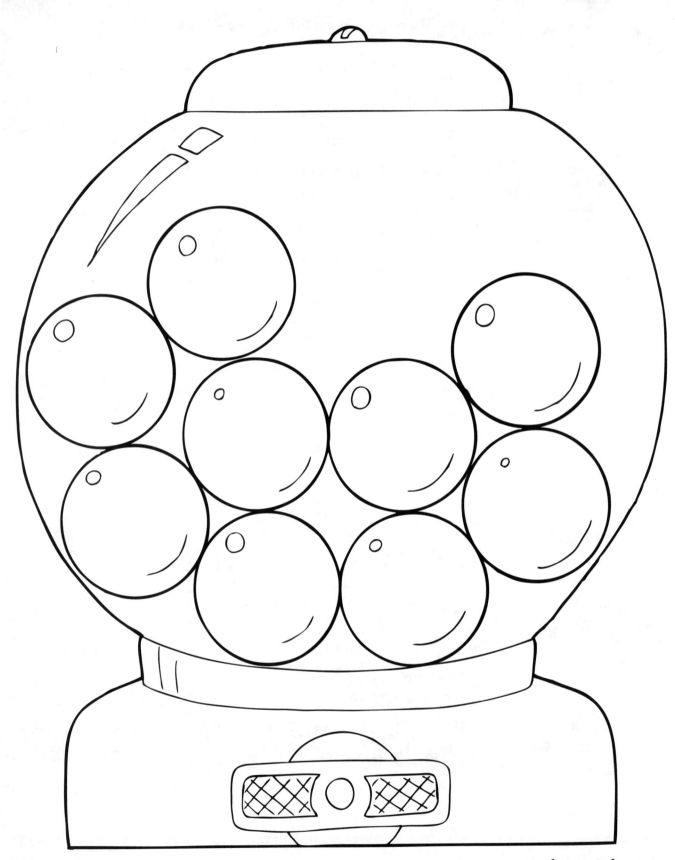

Match Mine: Mathematics
Kagan Publishing • 1 (800) 933-2667 • www.KaganOnline.com

Fractions—Naming

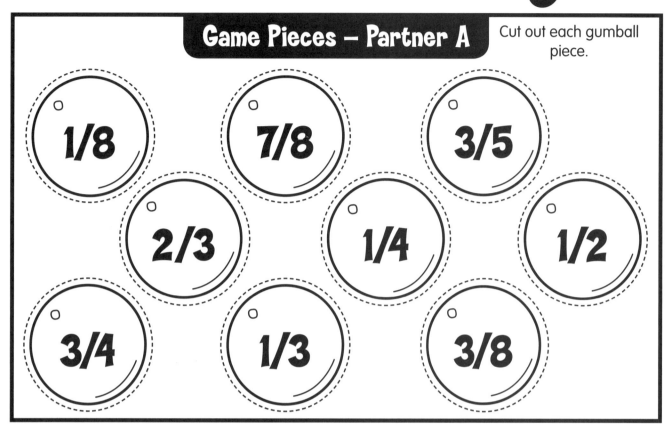

Game Pieces – Partner A
Cut out each gumball piece.

1/8   7/8   3/5

2/3   1/4   1/2

3/4   1/3   3/8

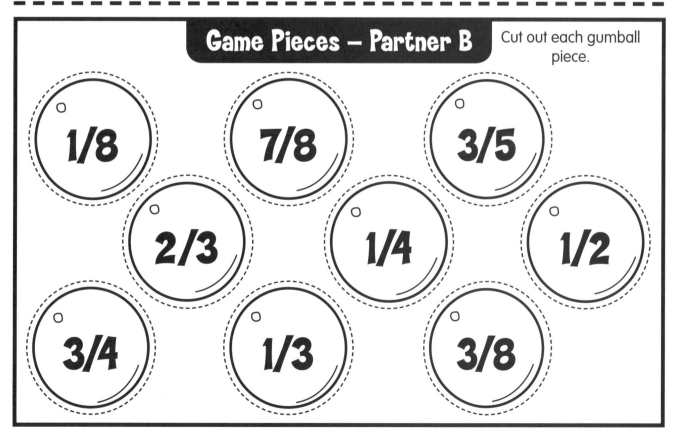

Game Pieces – Partner B
Cut out each gumball piece.

1/8   7/8   3/5

2/3   1/4   1/2

3/4   1/3   3/8

Geometry Terms

Partner A places geometry term pieces on the geometric shape game board. Partner B cooperates with Partner A to make a match.

Game Board

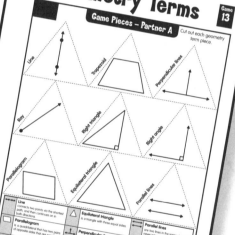

Game Pieces

Mathematics Vocabulary

- Equilateral triangle
- Line
- Line segment
- Parallel
- Parallelogram
- Perpendicular
- Polygon
- Quadrilateral
- Ray
- Right angle
- Right triangle
- Trapezoid

Challenger

The Sender must identify the item by its proper name as its location is described to the Receiver. For example, "The perpendicular lines are in the bottom right triangle."

Geometry Standard

Analyze characteristics and properties of two- and three-dimensional geometric shapes and develop mathematical arguments about geometric relationships.

Students should...
- identify, compare, and analyze attributes of two- and three-dimensional shapes and develop vocabulary to describe the attributes.

Geometry Terms

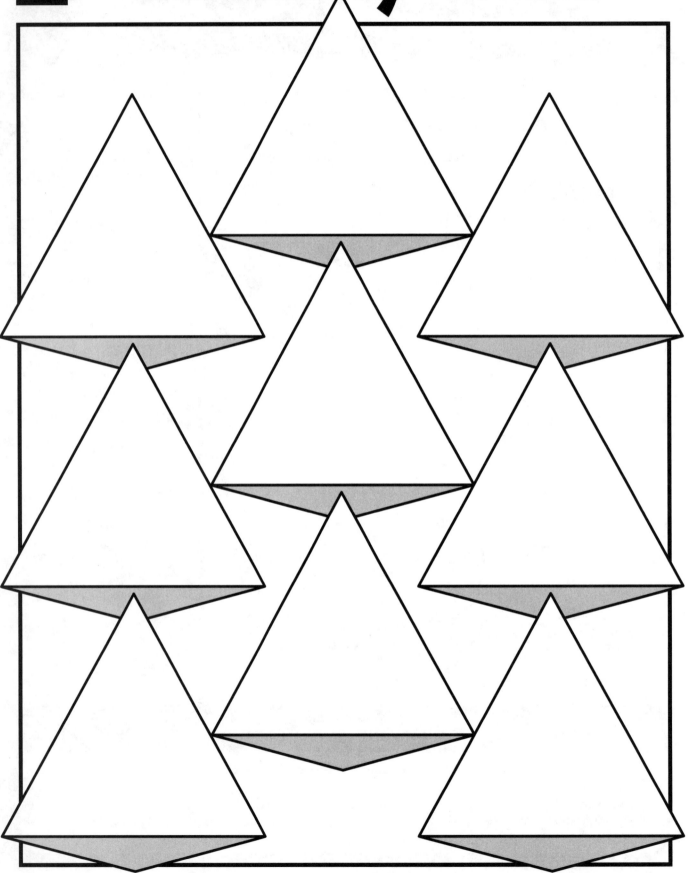

Match Mine: Mathematics
Kagan Publishing • 1 (800) 933-2667 • www.KaganOnline.com

Geometry Terms

Game Pieces – Partner A

Cut out each geometry term piece.

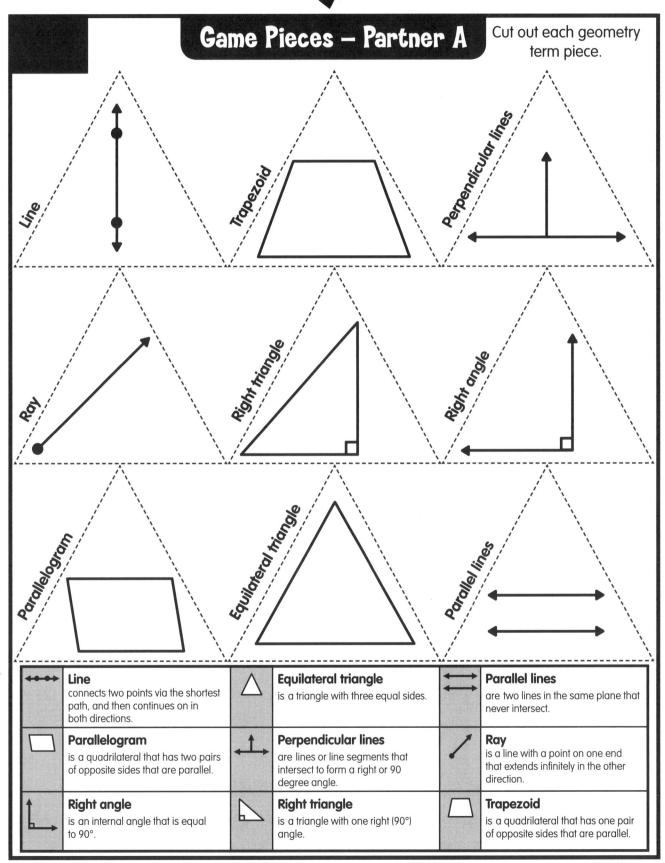

	Line connects two points via the shortest path, and then continues on in both directions.		**Equilateral triangle** is a triangle with three equal sides.		**Parallel lines** are two lines in the same plane that never intersect.
	Parallelogram is a quadrilateral that has two pairs of opposite sides that are parallel.		**Perpendicular lines** are lines or line segments that intersect to form a right or 90 degree angle.		**Ray** is a line with a point on one end that extends infinitely in the other direction.
	Right angle is an internal angle that is equal to 90°.		**Right triangle** is a triangle with one right (90°) angle.		**Trapezoid** is a quadrilateral that has one pair of opposite sides that are parallel.

Geometry Terms

Game Pieces – Partner B

Cut out each geometry term piece.

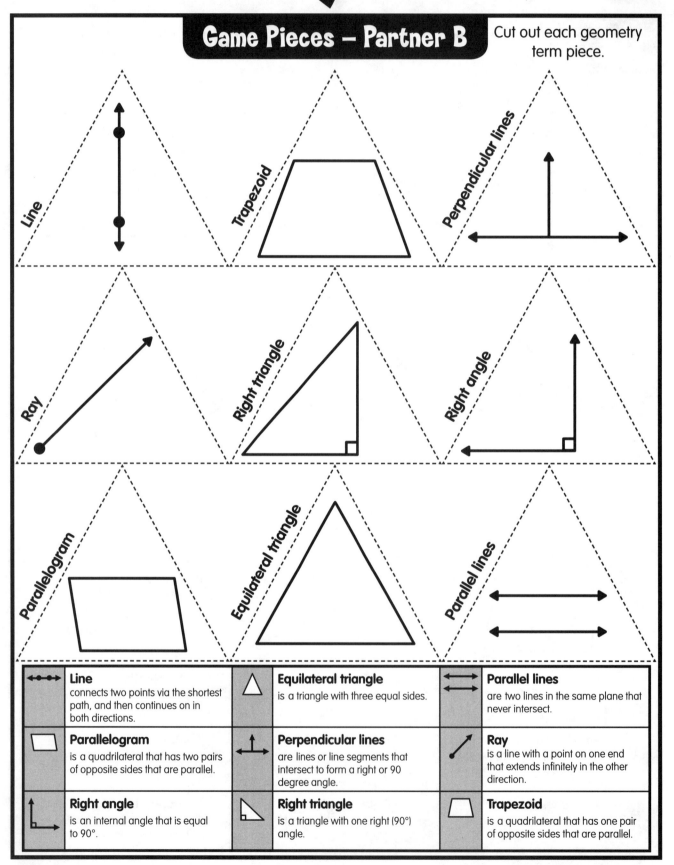

	Line		Equilateral triangle		Parallel lines
	connects two points via the shortest path, and then continues on in both directions.		is a triangle with three equal sides.		are two lines in the same plane that never intersect.
	Parallelogram		**Perpendicular lines**		**Ray**
	is a quadrilateral that has two pairs of opposite sides that are parallel.		are lines or line segments that intersect to form a right or 90 degree angle.		is a line with a point on one end that extends infinitely in the other direction.
	Right angle		**Right triangle**		**Trapezoid**
	is an internal angle that is equal to 90°.		is a triangle with one right (90°) angle.		is a quadrilateral that has one pair of opposite sides that are parallel.

Match Mine: Mathematics
Kagan Publishing • 1 (800) 933-2667 • www.KaganOnline.com

Graphs–Bar

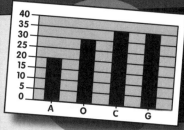

Partner A places bar graph pieces on the juice box game board. Partner B cooperates with Partner A to make a match.

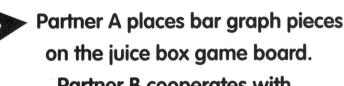

Game Board

Graphs–Bar

KEY: A=APPLE C=CHERRY G=GRAPE O=ORANGE

68

Game Pieces

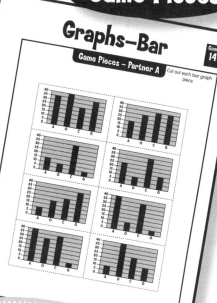

Graphs–Bar
Game Pieces – Partner A Cut out each bar graph piece.

69

Mathematics Vocabulary

- Bar
- Bar chart
- Bar graph
- Data
- Horizontal
- Key
- Length
- Plotting
- Vertical
- *x*-axis
- *y*-axis

Challenger

The Sender may not use actual bar lengths, and may only use the relationship of the bars to describe the bar graph to the Receiver. For example, "The graph that represents 4 times as many orange juices as apple juices is in the bottom left corner."

Data Analysis and Probability Standard

Formulate questions that can be addressed with data and collect, organize, and display relevant data to answer them.

Students should...
- represent data using tables and graphs such as line plots, bar graphs, and line graphs.

Graphs—Bar

KEY: A=APPLE   G=GRAPE
      C=CHERRY   O=ORANGE

Match Mine: Mathematics
Kagan Publishing • 1 (800) 933-2667 • www.KaganOnline.com

Graphs—Bar

Game Pieces – Partner A

Cut out each bar graph piece.

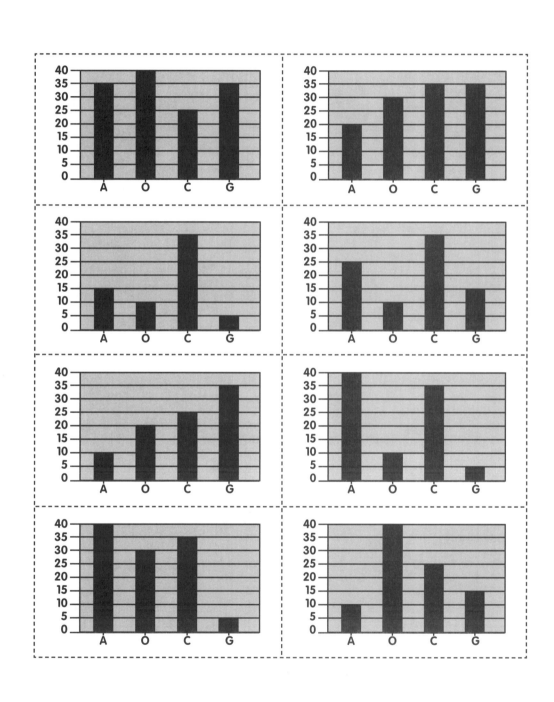

Graphs—Bar

Game Pieces – Partner B

Cut out each bar graph piece.

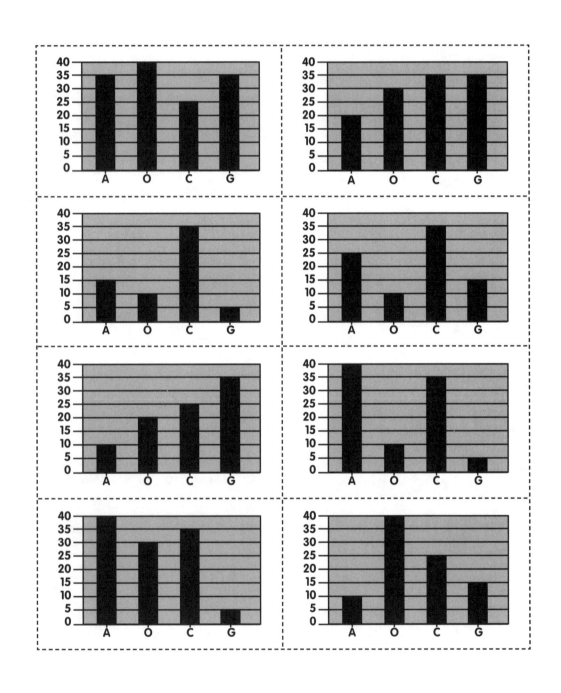

Match Mine: Mathematics
Kagan Publishing • 1 (800) 933-2667 • www.KaganOnline.com

Graphs—Line

Partner A places line graph pieces on the graph game board. Partner B cooperates with Partner A to make a match.

Game Board

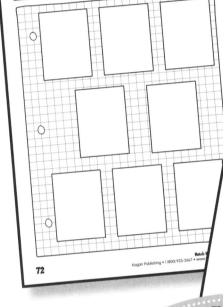

Game Pieces

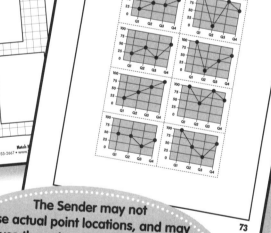

Mathematics Vocabulary

- Data
- Horizontal
- Line chart
- Line graph
- Peak
- Valley
- Vertical
- *x*-axis
- *y*-axis

Challenger

The Sender may not use actual point locations, and may only use the units of increase or decrease to describe the line graph to the Receiver. For example, "The graph that went up 25 units in Quarter 2, then stayed even for Quarter 3, is in the middle row on the left side."

Data Analysis and Probability Standard

Formulate questions that can be addressed with data and collect, organize, and display relevant data to answer them.

Students should...

- represent data using tables and graphs such as line plots, bar graphs, and line graphs.

Graphs—Line

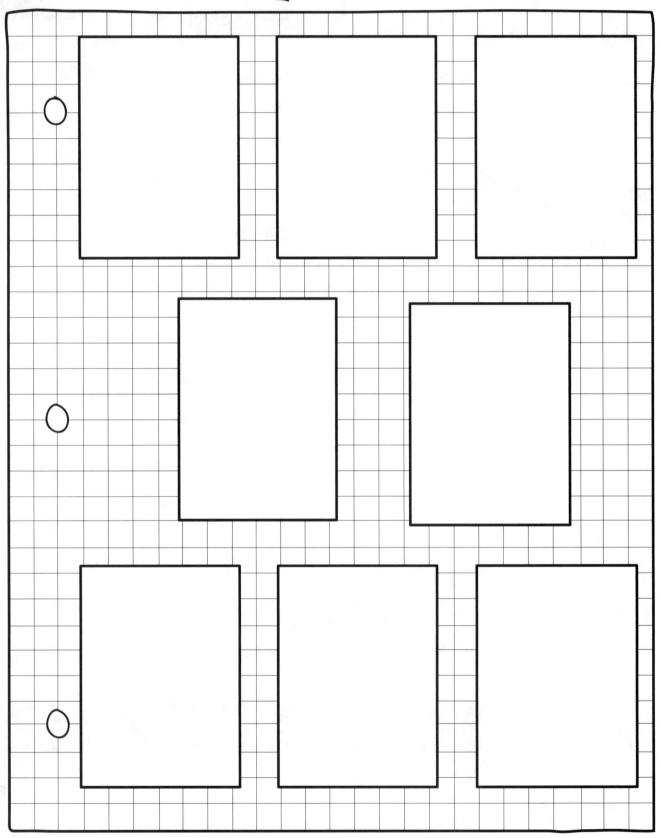

Graphs—Line

Game Pieces – Partner A

Cut out each line graph piece.

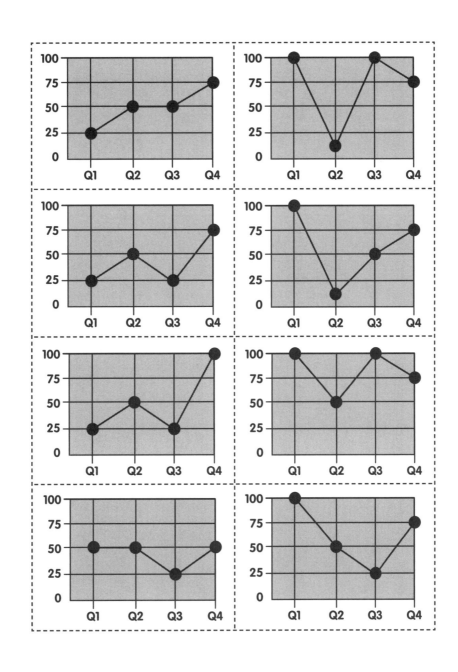

Graphs—Line

Cut out each line graph piece.

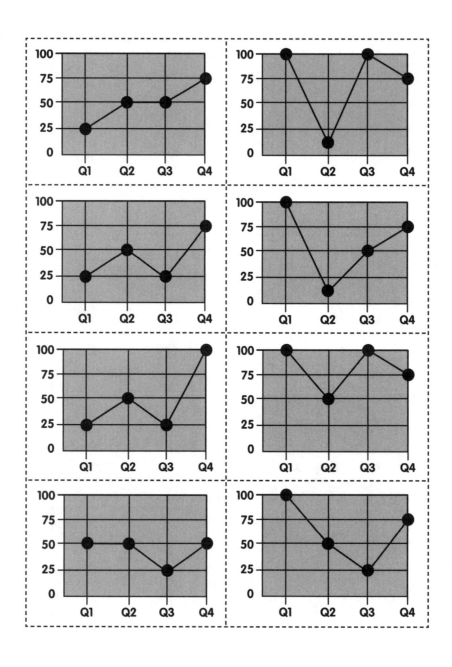

Graphs—Pie

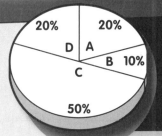

Partner A places pie graph pieces on the outer space game board. Partner B cooperates with Partner A to make a match.

Game Board

Graphs—Pie
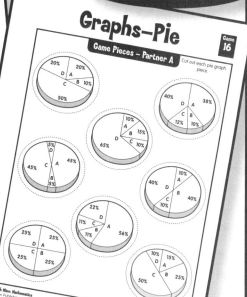

Game Pieces

Graphs—Pie
Game Pieces – Partner A

Mathematics Vocabulary

- Arc length
- Area
- Central angle
- Circle graph
- Percent
- Pie
- Pie chart
- Sector
- Slice

Challenger

The Sender may not use actual slice sizes, and may only use the relationship of the slices to describe the pie graph to the Receiver. For example, "The graph where all the slices are the same size is on the bottom right planet."

Data Analysis and Probability Standard

Formulate questions that can be addressed with data and collect, organize, and display relevant data to answer them.
Students should...
- represent data using tables and graphs such as line plots, bar graphs, and line graphs.

Graphs—Pie

A=EARTH — B=SATURN
C=JUPITER — D=MARS

Match Mine: Mathematics
Kagan Publishing • 1 (800) 933-2667 • www.KaganOnline.com

Graphs–Pie

Game Pieces – Partner A

Cut out each pie graph piece.

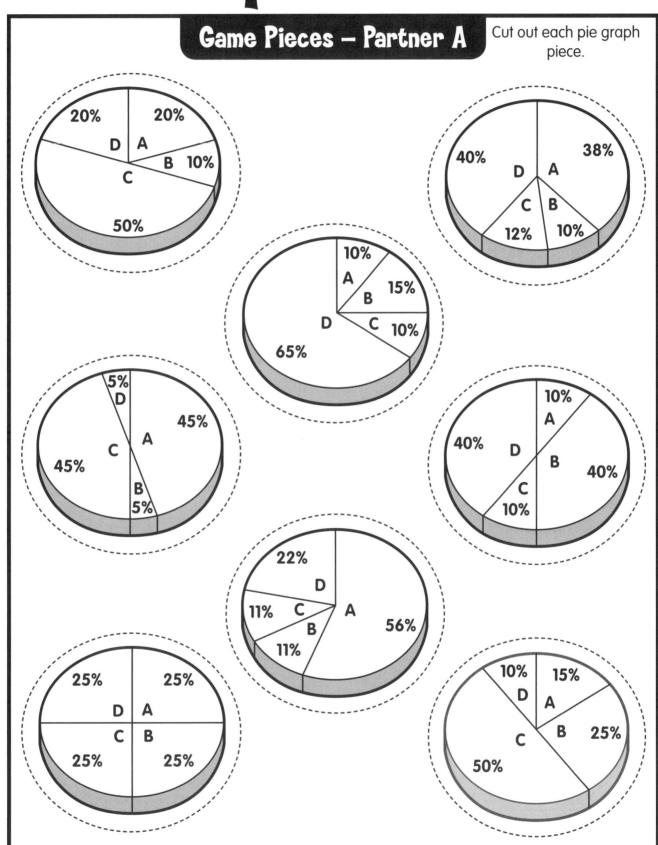

Graphs–Piece

Cut out each pie graph piece.

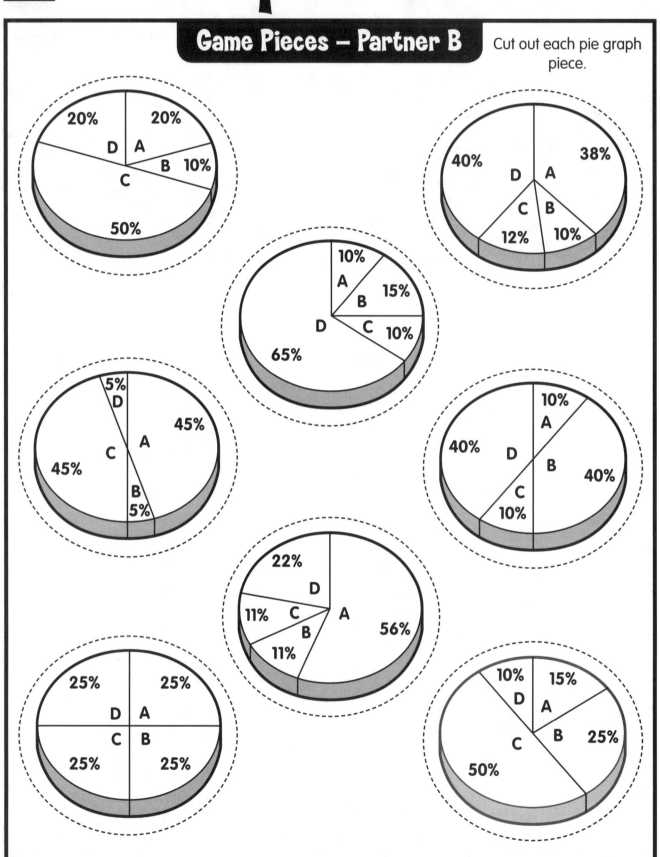

Match Mine: Mathematics
Kagan Publishing • 1 (800) 933-2667 • www.KaganOnline.com

Line Slope

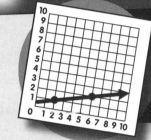

Partner A places line slope pieces on the ski slope game board. Partner B cooperates with Partner A to make a match.

Game Board

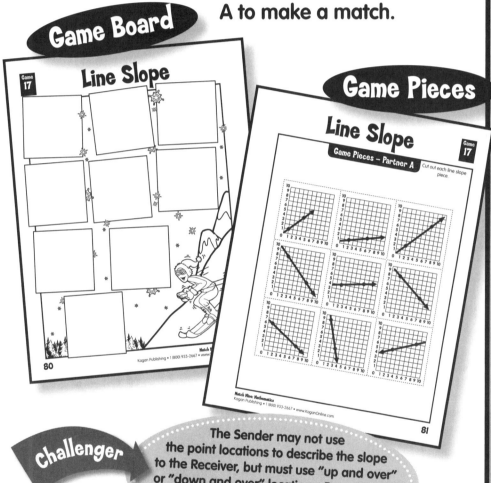

Game Pieces

Mathematics Vocabulary

- Angle
- Coordinates
- Down
- First point
- Horizontal
- Intersect
- Line
- Negative
- Point
- Positive
- Second point
- Slope
- Up
- Vertical
- *x*-Axis
- *y*-Axis

Challenger

The Sender may not use the point locations to describe the slope to the Receiver, but must use "up and over" or "down and over" locations. For example, "I'm looking at the piece where the slope is one up and right four over... "

Geometry Standard

Specify locations and describe spatial relationships using coordinate geometry and other representational systems.
Students should...
- make and use coordinate systems to specify locations and to describe paths.

Line Slope

Match Mine: Mathematics
Kagan Publishing • 1 (800) 933-2667 • www.KaganOnline.com

Line Slope

Game Pieces – Partner A

Cut out each line slope piece.

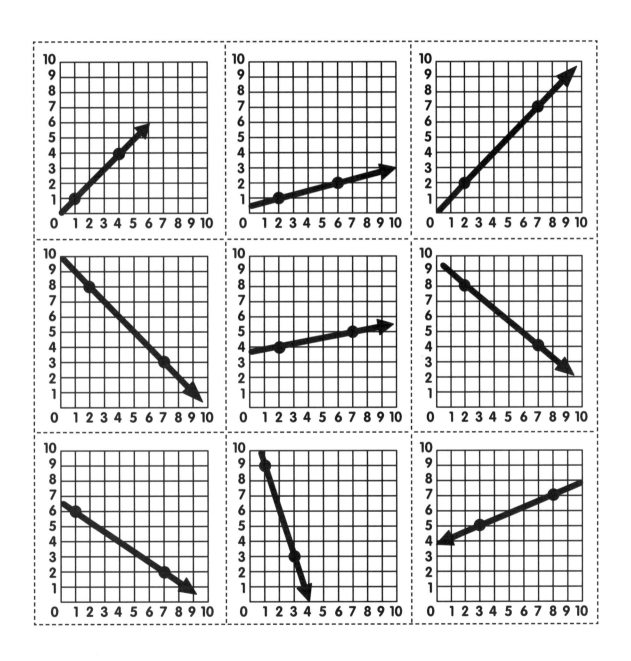

Line Slope

Game Pieces – Partner B

Cut out each line slope piece.

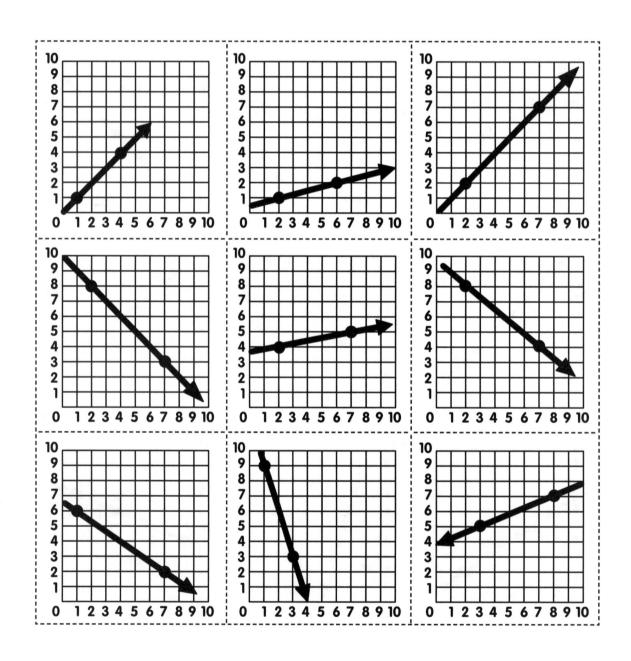

Match Mine: Mathematics
Kagan Publishing • 1 (800) 933-2667 • www.KaganOnline.com

Measuring

Partner A places worm pieces on the ruler game board. Partner B cooperates with Partner A to make a match.

Game Board

Measuring

1 in = 2.54 cm
1 cm = 0.394 in.

Game Pieces

Mathematics Vocabulary

- Centimeter(s)
- Inch(es)
- Length
- Long
- Measure
- Ruler

Challenger

The Sender must convert inches to centimeters or vice versa to describe the worm's length to the Receiver. For example, "The first worm is 6 1/4 inches long or 15.875 centimeters."

Measurement Standard

Apply appropriate techniques, tools, and formulas to determine measurements.
Students should...
- select and apply appropriate standard units and tools to measure length, area, volume, weight, time, temperature, and the size of angles.
- select and use benchmarks to estimate measurements.

Measuring

1 in	= 2.54 cm
1 cm	= 0.394 in.

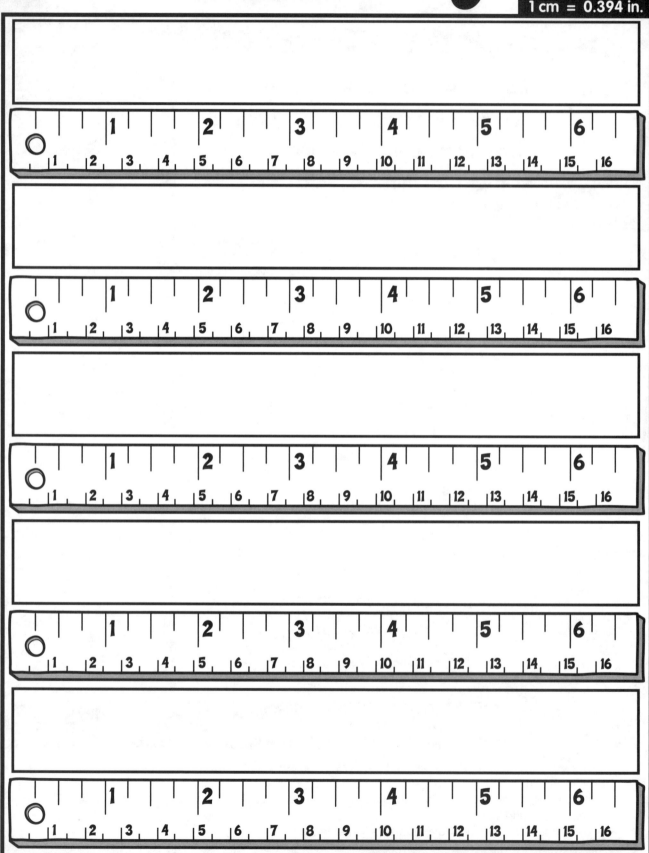

Match Mine: Mathematics
Kagan Publishing • 1 (800) 933-2667 • www.KaganOnline.com

Measuring

Game Pieces – Partner A

Cut out each worm piece.

Game Pieces – Partner B

Cut out each worm piece.

Money

Partner A places coin pieces on the piggy bank game board. Partner B cooperates with Partner A to make a match.

Game Board

Money

Game Pieces

Mathematics Vocabulary

- Cents
- Dime
- Nickel
- Penny
- Quarter

Challenger

The Sender may not state the value of the coins, but instead must state the value subtracted from one dollar. For example, if the coins add up to $0.20, then the Sender might say, "I'm looking at the piece that is 80¢... ."

Problem Solving Standard

Instructional programs from prekindergarten through grade 12:
Students should...
- solve problems that arise in mathematics and in other contexts.

Money

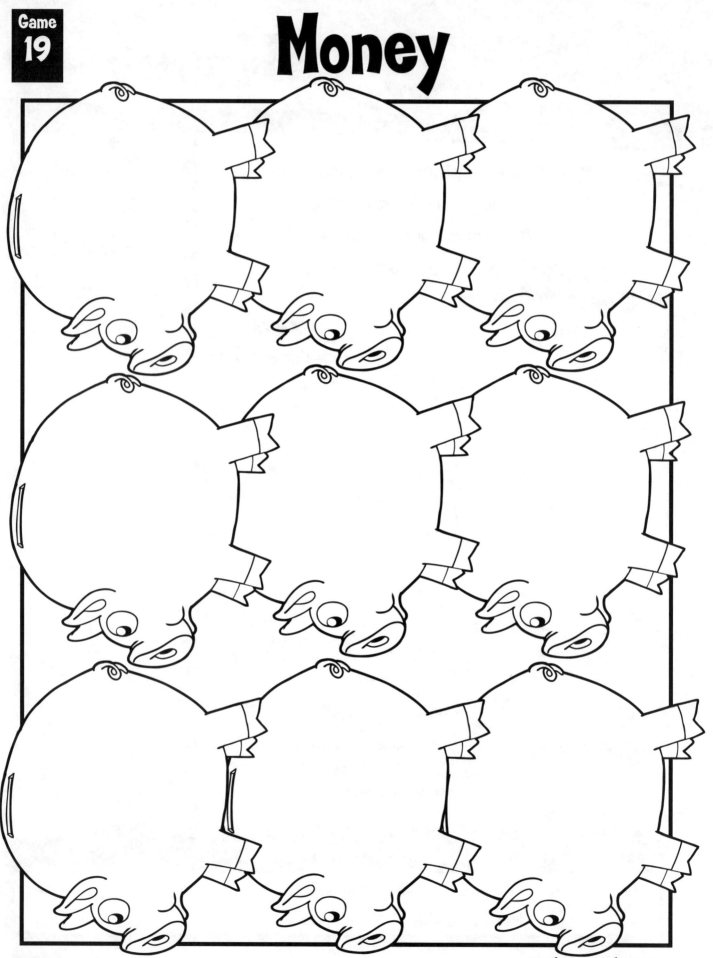

Match Mine: Mathematics
Kagan Publishing • 1 (800) 933-2667 • www.KaganOnline.com

Money

Game Pieces – Partner A

Cut out each set of coins.

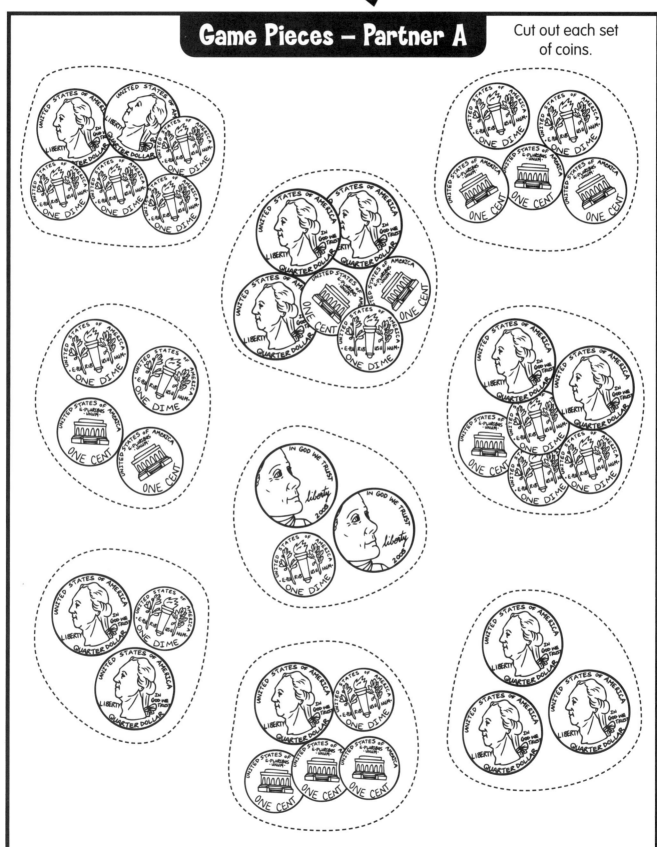

Money

Game Pieces – Partner B

Cut out each set of coins.

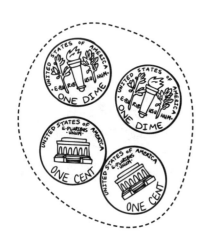

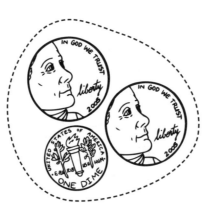

Match Mine: Mathematics
Kagan Publishing • 1 (800) 933-2667 • www.KaganOnline.com

Multiplication Grid

Partner A places multiplication grid pieces on the gifts game board. Partner B cooperates with Partner A to make a match.

Game Board

Multiplication Grid

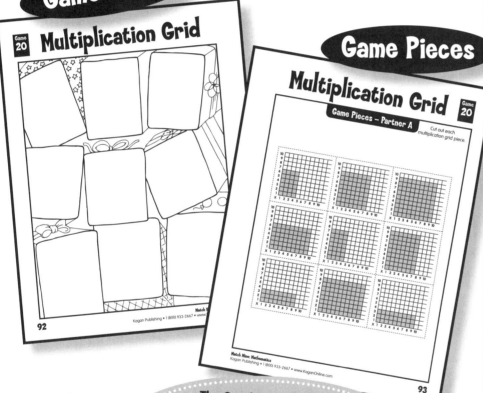

92

Game Pieces

Multiplication Grid
Game Pieces – Partner A

Cut out each multiplication grid piece.

Match Mine: Mathematics
Kagan Publishing • 1 (800) 933-2667 • www.KaganOnline.com

93

Mathematics Vocabulary

- By
- Column
- Grid
- Multiply
- Product
- Row
- Squares
- Times

Challenger

The Sender must state the multiplication problem each gird represents as its location is described to the Receiver. For example, "The grid that represents 7 x 9 = 63 is in the top center gift."

➕ Number and Operations Standard

Understand meanings of operations and how they relate to one another.
Students should...
- understand various meanings of multiplication and division.
- understand the effects of multiplying and dividing whole numbers.

Multiplication Grid

Match Mine: Mathematics
Kagan Publishing • 1 (800) 933-2667 • www.KaganOnline.com

Multiplication Grid

Cut out each multiplication grid piece.

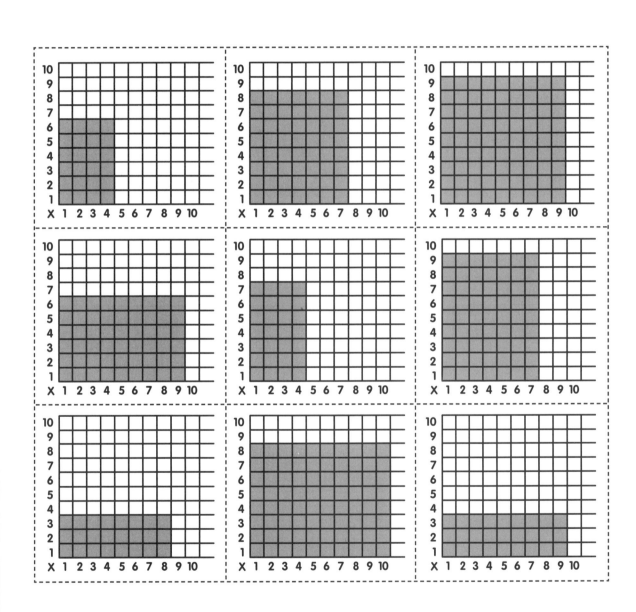

Multiplication Grid

Game Pieces – Partner B

Cut out each
multiplication grid piece.

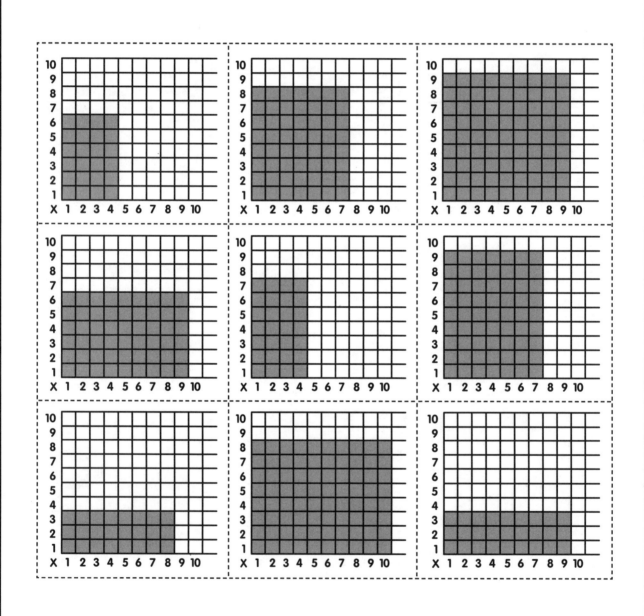

Match Mine: Mathematics
Kagan Publishing • 1 (800) 933-2667 • www.KaganOnline.com

Number Line

Partner A places number line pieces on the popsicle game board. Partner B cooperates with Partner A to make a match.

Game Board

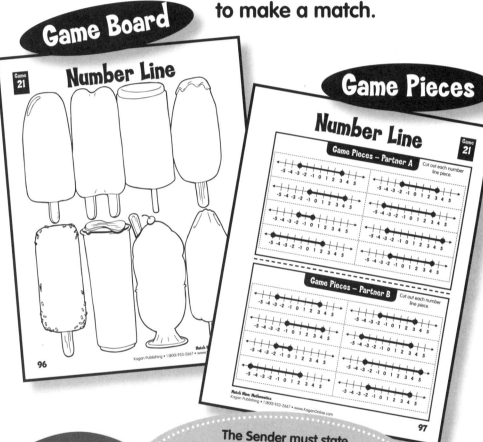

Game Pieces

Mathematics Vocabulary

- Negative
- Number line
- Point
- Positive

Challenger

The Sender must state the number line as a problem as its location is described to the Receiver. For example, if the number line has points at -2 and 3, the Sender might say, "The first number line represents the problem -2 + 3 = 1."

✚ Numbers and Operations Standard

Understand numbers, ways of representing numbers, relationships among numbers, and number systems. **Students should...**
- explore numbers less than 0 by extending the number line and through familiar applications.

Number Line

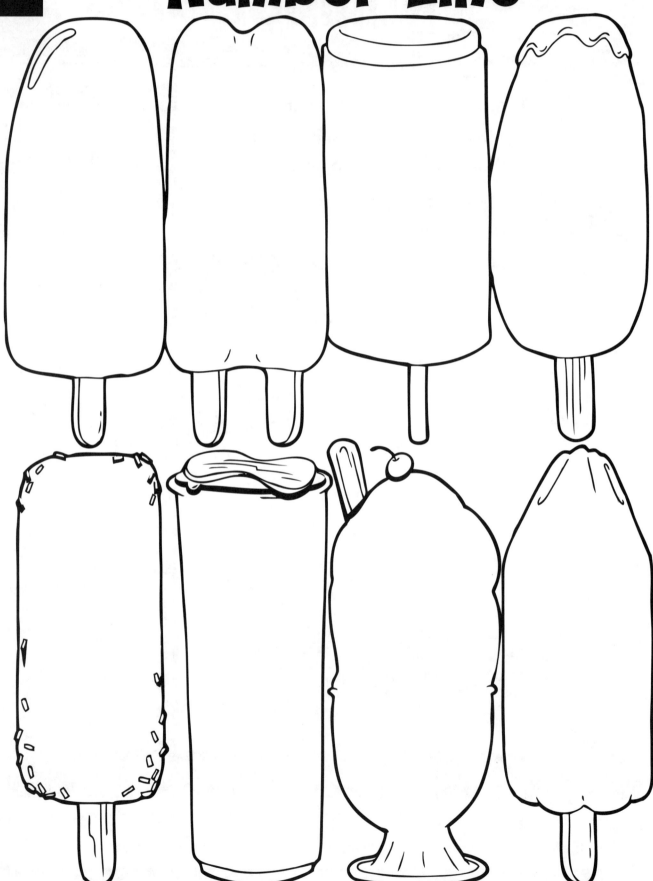

Match Mine: Mathematics
Kagan Publishing • 1 (800) 933-2667 • www.KaganOnline.com

Number Line

Game Pieces – Partner A

Cut out each number line piece.

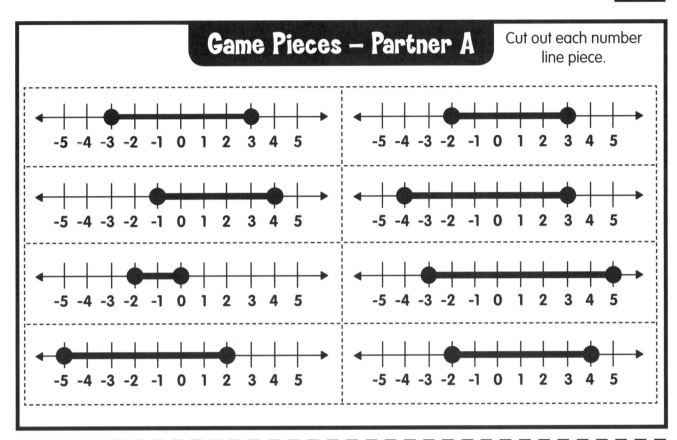

Game Pieces – Partner B

Cut out each number line piece.

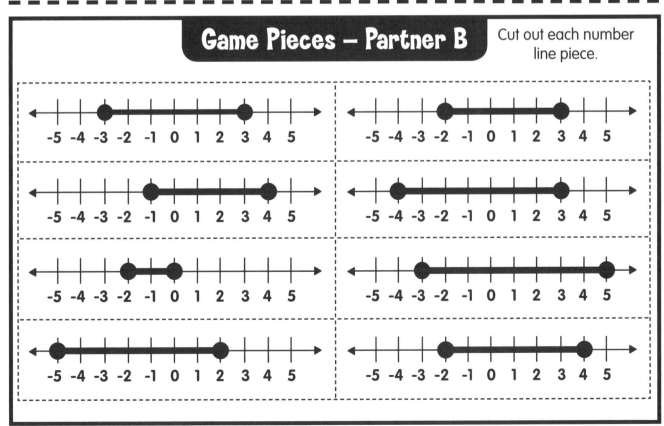

1,908,305

Partner A places high score number pieces on the video game board. Partner B cooperates with Partner A to make a match.

Mathematics Vocabulary

- Hundreds
- Hundred thousands
- Millions
- Ones
- Tens
- Ten Thousands
- Thousands

Game Board

Game 22

Numbers

HIGH SCORES

100

Game Pieces

Numbers

Game 22

Game Pieces – Partner A
Cut out each high score number piece.

1,980,305	1,980,035	1,890,035
1,809,530	1,890,305	1,809,503
1,980,503	1,980,350	1,089,503
1,908,350	1,089,350	1,908,305
1,890,305	1,890,053	1,089,530

Game Pieces – Partner B
Cut out each high score number piece.

1,980,305	1,980,035	1,890,035
1,809,530	1,089,305	1,809,503
1,980,503	1,980,350	1,089,503
1,908,350	1,089,350	1,908,305
1,890,305	1,890,053	1,089,530

Match Mine: Mathematics
Kagan Publishing • 1 (800) 933-2667 • www.KaganOnline.com

101

Challenger

The Sender must say the actual number, not just list the digits. For example the number 1,908,305 is expressed as "One million, nine hundred eight thousand, three hundred five."

✚ Number and Operations Standard

Understand numbers, ways of representing numbers, relationships among numbers, and number systems.
Students should...
- Understand the place-value structure of the base-ten number system and be able to represent and compare whole numbers and decimals.

Numbers

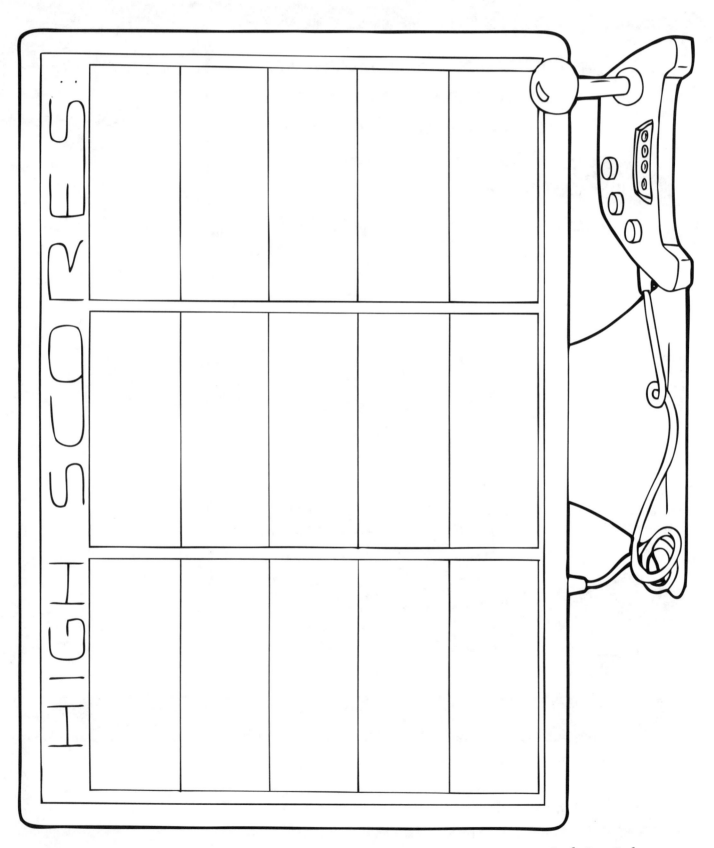

Match Mine: Mathematics
Kagan Publishing • 1 (800) 933-2667 • www.KaganOnline.com

Numbers

Game Pieces – Partner A
Cut out each high score number piece.

1,980,305	1,980,035	1,890,035
1,809,530	1,890,305	1,809,503
1,980,503	1,980,350	1,089,503
1,908,350	1,089,350	1,908,305
1,890,305	1,890,053	1,089,530

Game Pieces – Partner B
Cut out each high score number piece.

1,980,305	1,980,035	1,890,035
1,809,530	1,890,305	1,809,503
1,980,503	1,980,350	1,089,503
1,908,350	1,089,350	1,908,305
1,890,305	1,890,053	1,089,530

Partner A places jewel patterns on the belts game board. Partner B cooperates with Partner A to make a match.

Mathematics Vocabulary

- AB
- ABB
- AABB
- AAB
- ABBB
- ABC
- ABBC
- ABCC

Game Board

Patterns

Game Pieces

Patterns

Challenger

The Sender must identify the pattern rather than describing the jewel. For example, "The first pattern is AAB."

X= Algebra Standard

Understand patterns, relations, and functions.
Students should...
- describe, extend, and make generalizations about geometric and numeric patterns.
- represent and analyze patterns and functions, using words, tables, and graphs.

Patterns

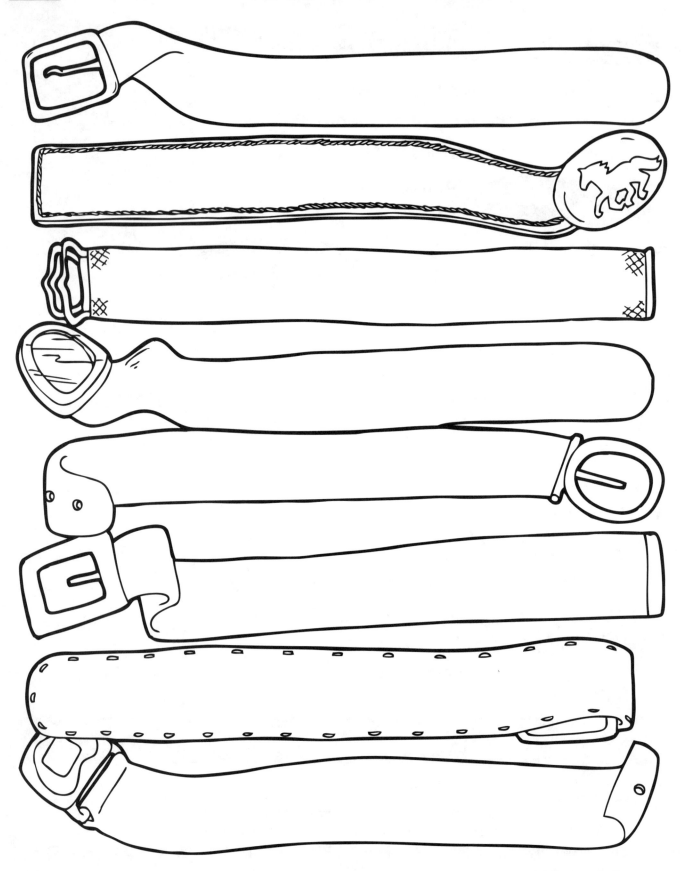

Match Mine: Mathematics
Kagan Publishing • 1 (800) 933-2667 • www.KaganOnline.com

Patterns

Game Pieces – Partner A

Cut out each jewel pattern piece.

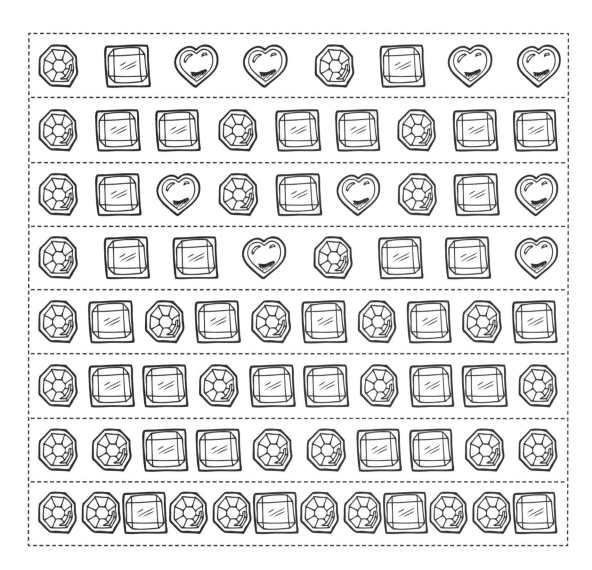

Patterns

Game Pieces – Partner B

Cut out each jewel
pattern piece.

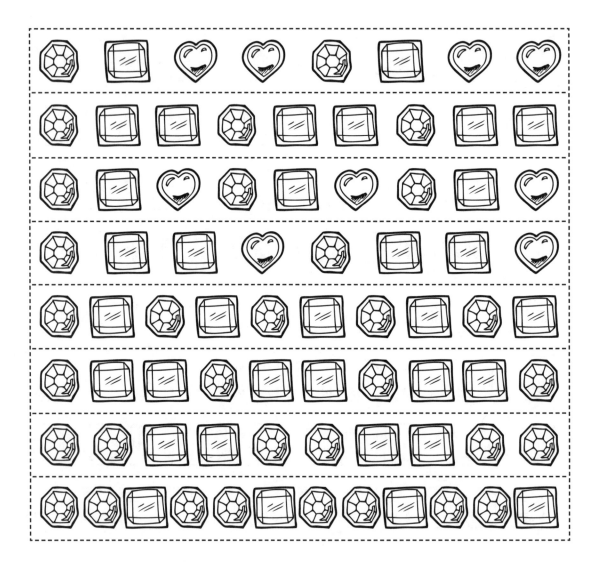

Place Value

Partner A places place value number pieces on the balloon game board. Partner B cooperates with Partner A to make a match.

99,9<u>9</u>9.999

Game Board

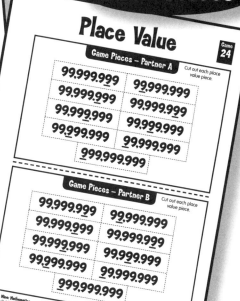

Place Value

Game Pieces

Place Value

Game Pieces – Partner A — Cut out each place value piece.

99.999.99<u>9</u>	9<u>9</u>.999.999
99.999.9<u>9</u>9	99.999.<u>9</u>99
99.9<u>9</u>9.999	99.99<u>9</u>.999
9<u>9</u>.999.999	99.999.9<u>9</u>9
999.999.999	

Game Pieces – Partner B — Cut out each place value piece.

99.999.<u>9</u>99	9<u>9</u>.999.999
99.999.9<u>9</u>9	99.999.999<u> </u>
99.9<u>9</u>9.999	99.99<u>9</u>.999
99.<u>9</u>99.999	99.<u>9</u>99.999
<u>9</u>99.999.999	

Mathematics Vocabulary

- Hundred thousands
- Hundreds
- Hundredths
- Ones
- Ten thousands
- Tens
- Tenths
- Thousands
- Thousandths

Place Value — Place Value Key

999,999.999

Hundred Thousands | Ten Thousands | Thousands | Hundreds | Tens | Ones | Tenths | Hundredths | Thousandths

Reference on page 110

Challenger

The Sender must describe the place value of the underlined number. For example, "The number with the underlined 9 in the one's place is in the first balloon."

✚ Numbers and Operation Standard

Understand numbers, ways of representing numbers, relationships among numbers, and number systems.
Students should...
- understand the place-value structure of the base-ten number system and be able to represent and compare whole numbers and decimals.

Place Value

Place Value

Game Pieces – Partner A

Cut out each place value piece.

99,999.9<u>9</u>9	9<u>9</u>,999.999
99,999.9<u>9</u>9	99,999.99<u>9</u>
99,99<u>9</u>.999	99,9<u>9</u>9.999
99,<u>9</u>99.999	<u>9</u>9,999.999

<u>9</u>99,999.999

Game Pieces – Partner B

Cut out each place value piece.

99,999.9<u>9</u>9	9<u>9</u>,999.999
99,999.<u>9</u>99	99,999.99<u>9</u>
99,99<u>9</u>.999	99,9<u>9</u>9.999
99,<u>9</u>99.999	<u>9</u>9,999.999

<u>9</u>99,999.999

Place Value

Place Value Key

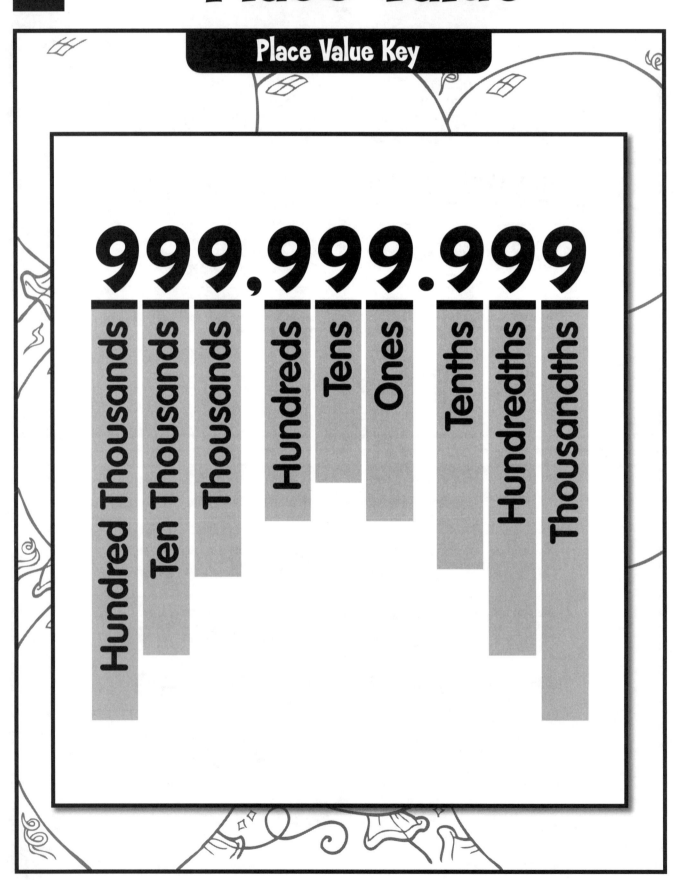

Match Mine: Mathematics
Kagan Publishing • 1 (800) 933-2667 • www.KaganOnline.com

Partner A places quadrilateral pieces on the quadrilateral game board. Partner B cooperates with Partner A to make a match.

Game Board

Game Pieces

Mathematics Vocabulary

- Concave quadrilateral
- Kite
- Parallelogram
- Rectangle
- Rhombus
- Square
- Trapezium
- Trapezoid

Challenger

The Sender must identify the quadrilateral by its proper name as its location is described to the Receiver. For example, "The rhombus is in the first row, second column."

Geometry Standard

Analyze characteristics and properties of two- and three-dimensional geometric shapes and develop mathematical arguments about geometric relationships.

Students should...

- identify, compare, and analyze attributes of two- and three-dimensional shapes and develop vocabulary to describe the attributes.
- classify two- and three-dimensional shapes according to their properties and develop definitions of classes of shapes such as triangles and pyramids.

Quadrilaterals

Match Mine: Mathematics
Kagan Publishing • 1 (800) 933-2667 • www.KaganOnline.com

Quadrilaterals

Game Pieces – Partner A

Cut out each quadrilateral piece.

Parallelogram

Rectangle

Square

Trapezoid

Kite

Concave quadrilateral

Rhombus

Trapezium

	Concave quadrilateral has an inward angle on its surface.			**Rhombus** is a parallelogram with four equal sides.
	Kite has two pairs of adjacent sides that are equal.			**Square** has two pairs of parallel sides, four right angles, and all four sides are equal. It is also a rectangle and a parallelogram.
	Parallelogram has two parallel pairs of opposite sides.			**Trapezium** has no parallel sides.
	Rectangle has two pairs of opposite sides parallel, and four right angles. It is also a parallelogram.			**Trapezoid** has one pair of parallel sides.

Quadrilaterals

Game Pieces – Partner B

Cut out each quadrilateral piece.

Parallelogram

Rectangle

Square

Trapezoid

Kite

Concave quadrilateral

Rhombus

Trapezium

	Concave quadrilateral has an inward angle on its surface.		**Rhombus** is a parallelogram with four equal sides.
	Kite has two pairs of adjacent sides that are equal.		**Square** has two pairs of parallel sides, four right angles, and all four sides are equal. It is also a rectangle and a parallelogram.
	Parallelogram has two parallel pairs of opposite sides.		**Trapezium** has no parallel sides.
	Rectangle has two pairs of opposite sides parallel, and four right angles. It is also a parallelogram.		**Trapezoid** has one pair of parallel sides.

Match Mine: Mathematics
Kagan Publishing • 1 (800) 933-2667 • www.KaganOnline.com

Roman Numerals

Partner A places Roman numeral pieces on the Roman columns game board. Partner B cooperates with Partner A to make a match.

Mathematics Vocabulary

- I = 1
- V = 5
- X = 10
- L = 50
- C = 100
- D = 500
- M = 1,000
- Arabic numeral
- Numeral numeral

Game Board

Roman Numerals

116

Game Pieces

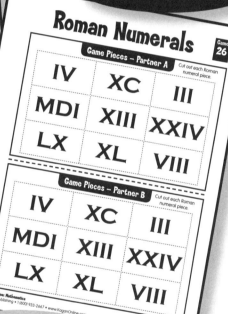

Roman Numerals

Game Pieces – Partner A
Cut out each Roman numeral piece.

IV	XC	III
MDI	XIII	XXIV
LX	XL	VIII

Game Pieces – Partner B
Cut out each Roman numeral piece.

IV	XC	III
MDI	XIII	XXIV
LX	XL	VIII

Match Mine: Mathematics
Kagan Publishing • 1 (800) 933-2667 • www.KaganOnline.com

117

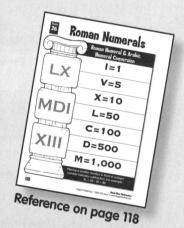

Roman Numerals
Roman Numeral & Arabic Numeral Conversion

LX	I = 1
	V = 5
MDI	X = 10
	L = 50
XIII	C = 100
	D = 500
	M = 1,000

118

Reference on page 118

Challenger

The Sender must identify the Roman numeral by stating what the Roman numeral would be if you added 25 (or any other number) to the number. For example, if the Roman numeral was IV, the Sender might say, "The new Roman numeral is XXIX."

Problem Solving Standard

Instructional programs from prekindergarten through grade 12:
Students should...
- solve problems that arise in mathematics and in other contexts.

Roman Numerals

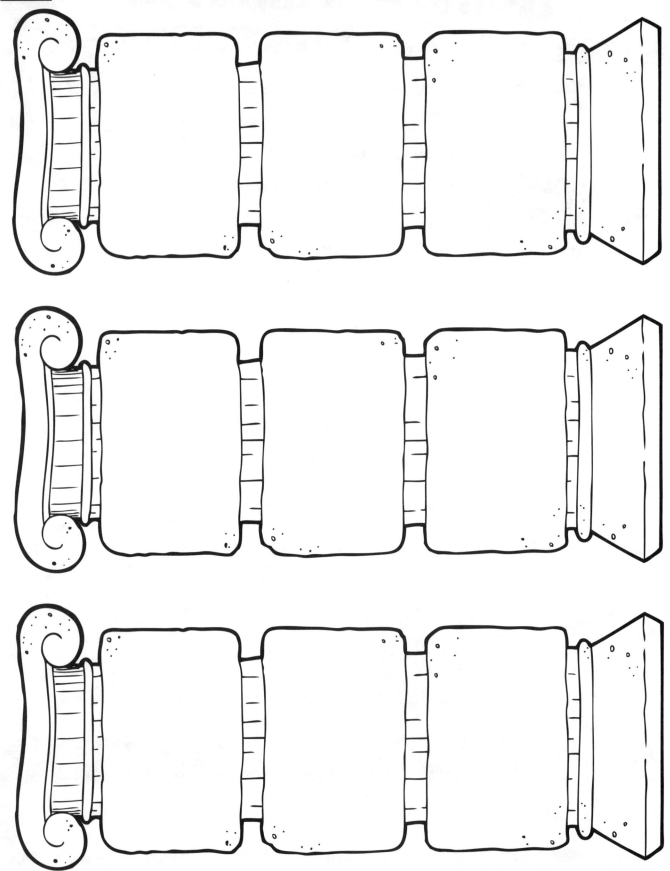

Match Mine: Mathematics
Kagan Publishing • 1 (800) 933-2667 • www.KaganOnline.com

Roman Numerals

Game Pieces – Partner A

Cut out each Roman numeral piece.

IV	XC	III
MDI	XIII	XXIV
LX	XL	VIII

Game Pieces – Partner B

Cut out each Roman numeral piece.

IV	XC	III
MDI	XIII	XXIV
LX	XL	VIII

Roman Numerals

Roman Numeral & Arabic Numeral Conversion

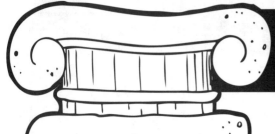

LX

MDI

XIII

| I = 1 |
| V = 5 |
| X = 10 |
| L = 50 |
| C = 100 |
| D = 500 |
| M = 1,000 |

Placing a smaller number in front of a larger number indicates subtraction. For example:
XL = 50 - 10 = 40

Match Mine: Mathematics
Kagan Publishing • 1 (800) 933-2667 • www.KaganOnline.com

Solid Geometry

Partner A places solid pieces on the toy blocks game board. Partner B cooperates with Partner A to make a match.

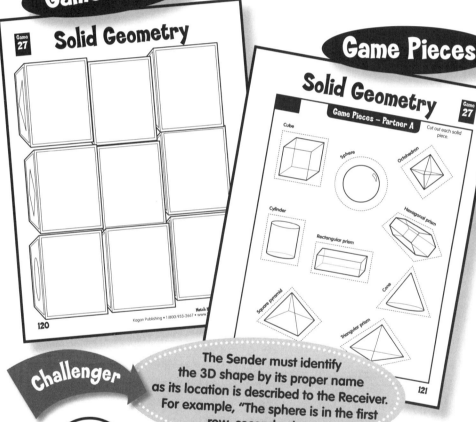

Game Board

Game Pieces

Mathematics Vocabulary

- 3-D
- Cone
- Cube
- Cylinder
- Hexagonal prism
- Octahedron
- Rectangular prism
- Solid geometry
- Sphere
- Square pyramid
- Three-dimensional
- Triangular prism

Challenger

The Sender must identify the 3D shape by its proper name as its location is described to the Receiver. For example, "The sphere is in the first row, second column."

Geometry Standard

Analyze characteristics and properties of two- and three-dimensional geometric shapes and develop mathematical arguments about geometric relationships.

Students should...

- identify, compare, and analyze attributes of two- and three-dimensional shapes and develop vocabulary to describe the attributes.
- classify two- and three-dimensional shapes according to their properties and develop definitions of classes of shapes such as triangles and pyramids.

Solid Geometry

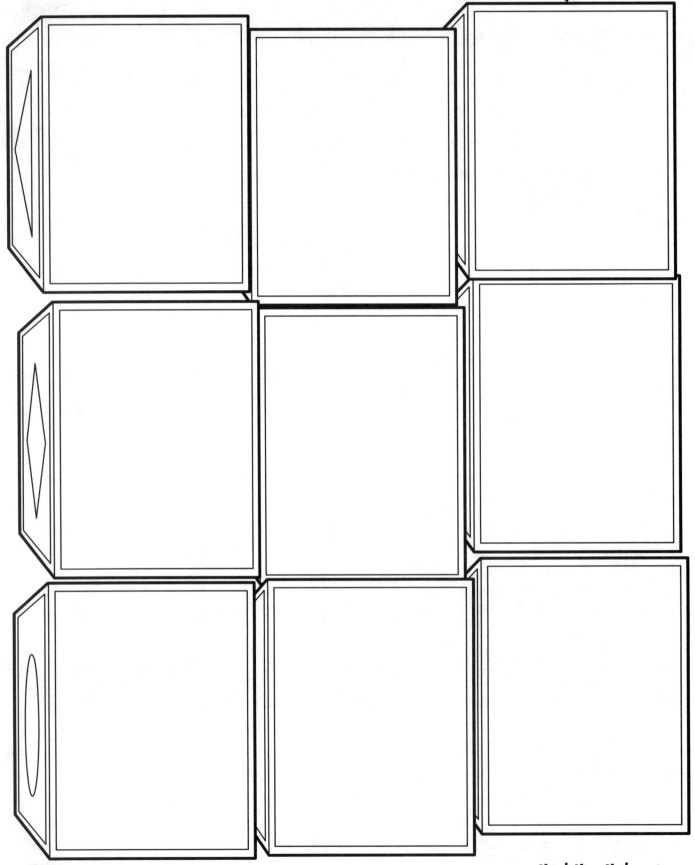

Match Mine: Mathematics
Kagan Publishing • 1 (800) 933-2667 • www.KaganOnline.com

Solid Geometry

Game Pieces – Partner A

Cut out each solid piece.

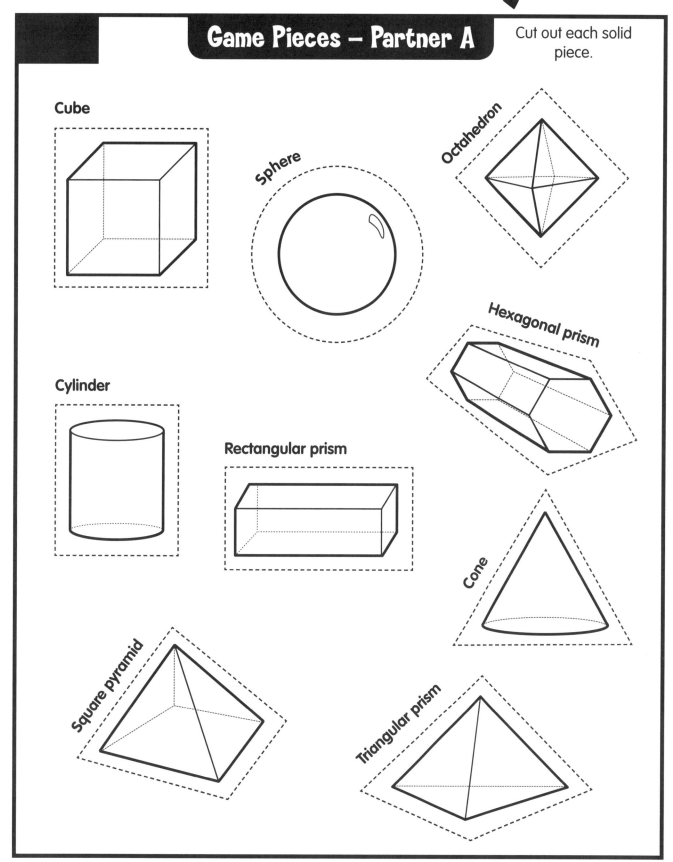

Cube

Sphere

Octahedron

Cylinder

Rectangular prism

Hexagonal prism

Cone

Square pyramid

Triangular prism

Solid Geometry

Cut out each
solid piece.

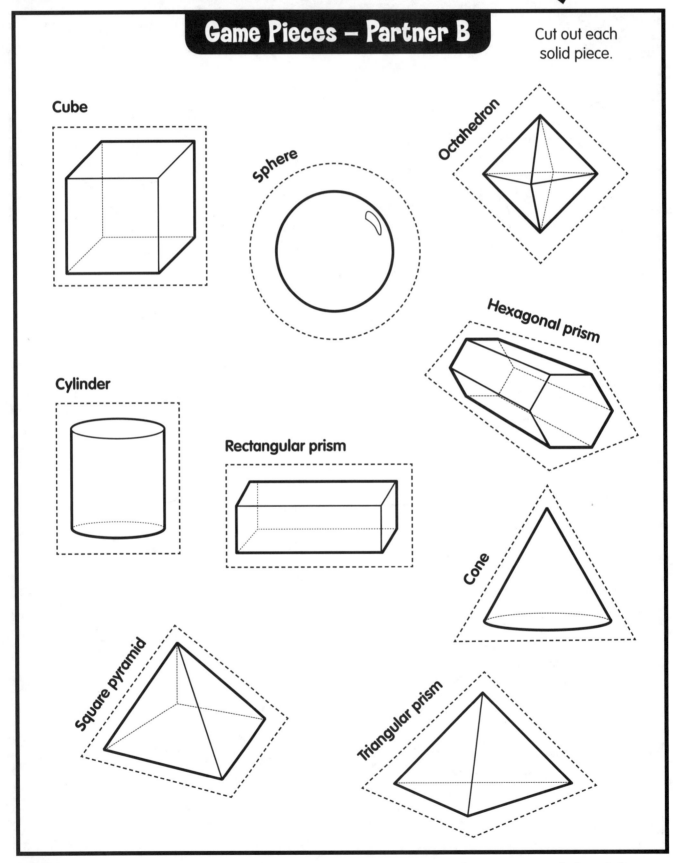

Cube

Sphere

Octahedron

Cylinder

Rectangular prism

Hexagonal prism

Cone

Square pyramid

Triangular prism

Match Mine: Mathematics
Kagan Publishing • 1 (800) 933-2667 • www.KaganOnline.com

Temperature

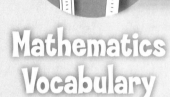

Partner A places thermometer pieces on the thermometer game board. Partner B cooperates with Partner A to make a match.

Game Board

Temperature

Temperature Celsius = $(5/9) \times (T_f - 32)$

Temperature Fahrenheit = $(9/5) \times (T_c + 32)$

124

Kagan Publishing • 1 (800) 933-2667 • www...

Game Pieces

Temperature

Game Pieces – Partner A

Cut out each thermometer piece.

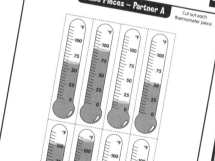

Match Mine: Mathematics
Kagan Publishing • 1 (800) 933-2667 • www.KaganOnline.com

125

Mathematics Vocabulary

- Cold
- Conversion
- Convert
- Degrees
- Fahrenheit
- Heat
- Hot
- Temperature
- Thermometer

Challenger

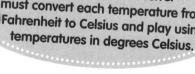

The Sender and Receiver must convert each temperature from Fahrenheit to Celsius and play using temperatures in degrees Celsius.

Measurement Standard

Apply appropriate techniques, tools, and formulas to determine measurements:
Students should...

- select and apply appropriate standard units and tools to measure length, area, volume, weight, time, temperature, and the size of angles.

Temperature

Temperature Celsius = $(5/9) \times (T_f - 32)$

Temperature Fahrenheit = $(9/5) \times T_c + 32$

Match Mine: Mathematics
Kagan Publishing • 1 (800) 933-2667 • www.KaganOnline.com

Temperature

Game Pieces – Partner A

Cut out each thermometer piece.

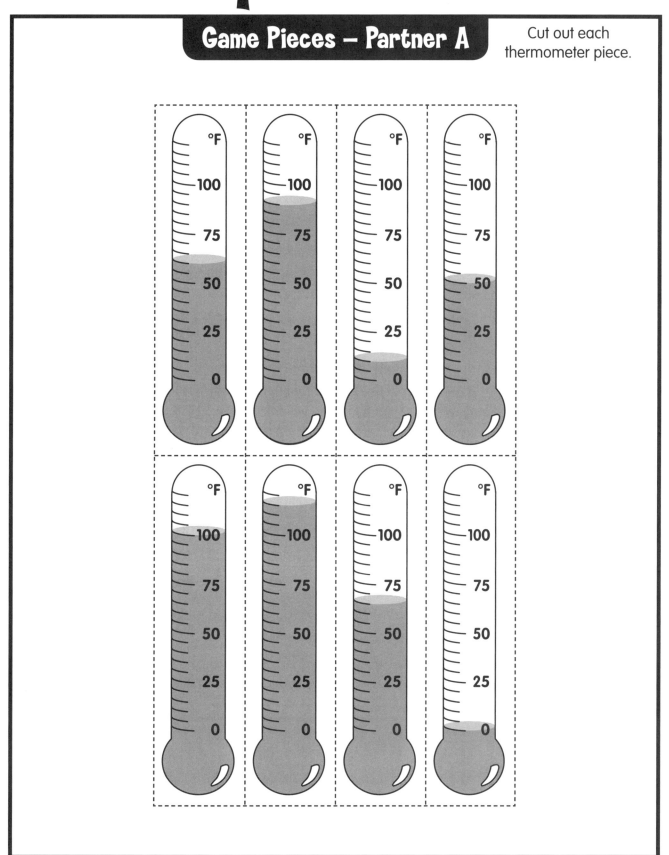

Temperature

Game Pieces – Partner B

Cut out each
thermometer piece.

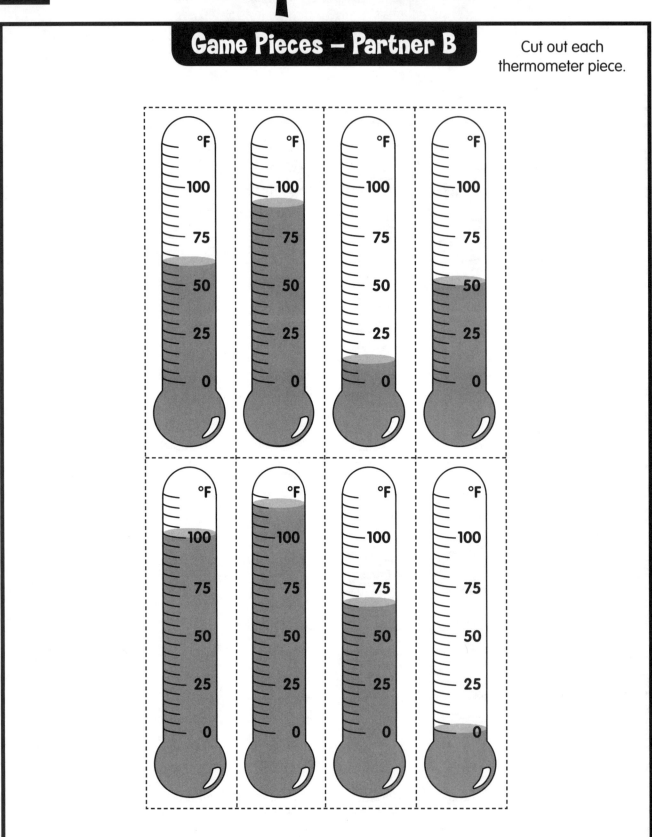

Match Mine: Mathematics
Kagan Publishing • 1 (800) 933-2667 • www.KaganOnline.com

Partner A places time pieces on the clock game board. Partner B cooperates with Partner A to make a match.

Game Board

Game Pieces

Mathematics Vocabulary

- Fifteen 'til
- Fifteen (:15)
- Forty-five (:45)
- Half past (:30)
- o'clock
- Quarter past (:15)
- Quarter til (:45)
- Thirty (:30)

Challenger

The Sender must identify the time by stating what the time would be if you added 15 minutes (or any other time) to the original time. For example, if the time was 8:45, the Sender might say, "The new time is 9:00."

Measurement Standard

Apply appropriate techniques, tools, and formulas to determine measurements:
Students should...
- select and apply appropriate standard units and tools to measure length, area, volume, weight, time, temperature, and the size of angles.

Time

Match Mine: Mathematics
Kagan Publishing • 1 (800) 933-2667 • www.KaganOnline.com

Time

Game Pieces – Partner A

Cut out each time clock piece.

Time

Game Pieces – Partner B

Cut out each time clock piece.

Match Mine: Mathematics
Kagan Publishing • 1 (800) 933-2667 • www.KaganOnline.com

Triangles

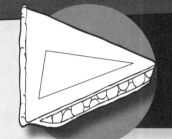

Partner A places triangle pieces on the pie game board. Partner B cooperates with Partner A to make a match.

Game Board

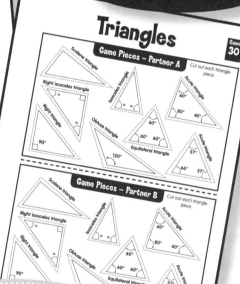

Triangles

Game Pieces

Mathematics Vocabulary

- Acute triangle
- Equilateral triangle
- Isosceles triangle
- Obtuse triangle
- Right Isosceles triangle
- Right triangle
- Scalene triangle

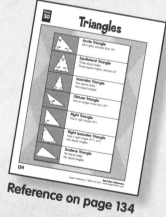

Reference on page 134

Challenger

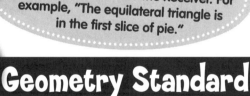

The Sender must identify the triangle by its proper name as its location is described to the Receiver. For example, "The equilateral triangle is in the first slice of pie."

Geometry Standard

Analyze characteristics and properties of two- and three-dimensional geometric shapes and develop mathematical arguments about geometric relationships.

Students should...

- identify, compare, and analyze attributes of two- and three-dimensional shapes and develop vocabulary to describe the attributes.
- classify two- and three-dimensional shapes according to their properties and develop definitions of classes of shapes such as triangles and pyramids.

Triangles

Triangles

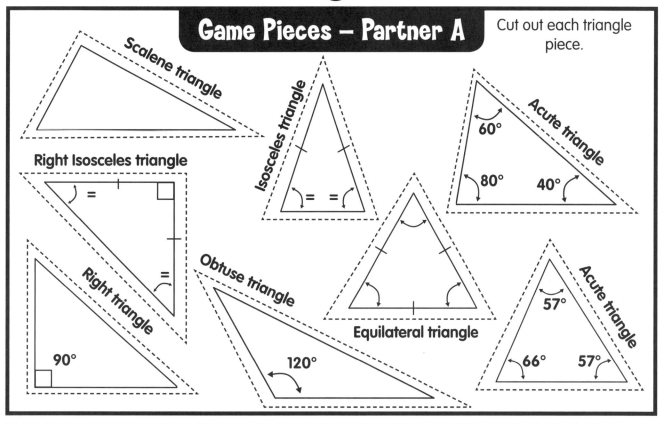

Game Pieces – Partner A

Cut out each triangle piece.

- Scalene triangle
- Right Isosceles triangle
- Isosceles triangle
- Acute triangle (60°, 80°, 40°)
- Equilateral triangle
- Right triangle (90°)
- Obtuse triangle (120°)
- Acute triangle (57°, 66°, 57°)

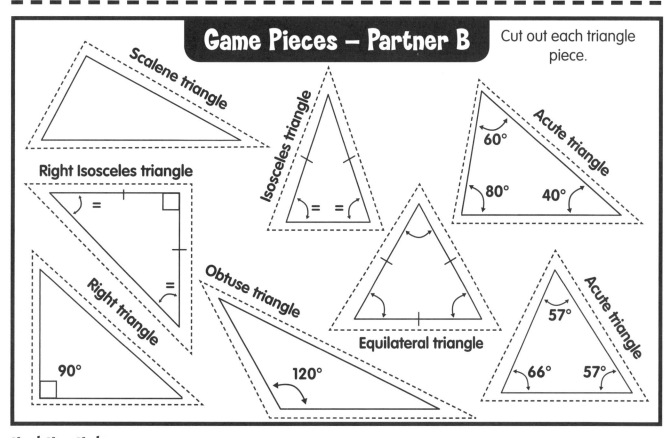

Game Pieces – Partner B

Cut out each triangle piece.

- Scalene triangle
- Right Isosceles triangle
- Isosceles triangle
- Acute triangle (60°, 80°, 40°)
- Equilateral triangle
- Right triangle (90°)
- Obtuse triangle (120°)
- Acute triangle (57°, 66°, 57°)

Triangles

Acute Triangle
All angles are less than 90°.

Equilateral Triangle
Three equal sides.
Three equal angles, always 60°.

Isosceles Triangle
Two equal sides.
Two equal angles.

Obtuse Triangle
Has an angle more than 90°.

Right Triangle
Has a right angle (90°).

Right Isosceles Triangle
Has a right angle (90°), and
two equal angles.

Scalene Triangle
No equal sides.
No equal angles.

Match Mine: Mathematics
Kagan Publishing • 1 (800) 933-2667 • www.KaganOnline.com